D1030791

Other books by MEINDERT DEJONG:

ALONG CAME A DOG
BILLY AND THE UNHAPPY BULL
THE CAT THAT WALKED A WEEK
DIRK'S DOG BELLO
GOOD LUCK DUCK
THE HOUSE OF SIXTY FATHERS
HURRY HOME, CANDY
THE LITTLE COW AND THE TURTLE
SHADRACH
SMOKE ABOVE THE LANE
THE TOWER BY THE SEA
THE WHEEL ON THE SCHOOL

THE MIGHTY ONES

THE MIGHTY ONES

(*Great Men and Women of Early Bible Days*)

by MEINDERT DEJONG

Pictures by HARVEY SCHMIDT

HARPER & BROTHERS *Publishers* NEW YORK

THE MIGHTY ONES

Printed in the United States of America

The Library of Congress catalog entry for this book appears at the end of the text.

All for JOHN RIPSTRA
And then for John's TIMMY

Contents

THE MIGHTY ONES

P R O L O G U E

Now faith is the substance of things hoped for, the evidence of things not seen.
By faith Abel offered unto God a more excellent sacrifice than Cain: and by it he being dead yet speaketh.
By faith Enoch was translated that he should not see death; and was not found, because God had translated him.
By faith Noah, being warned of God, prepared an ark to the saving of his house; by the which he condemned the world.
By faith Sarah was delivered of a child when she was past age, because she judged Him faithful who had promised.
By faith Abraham, when he was tried, offered up Isaac, his only begotten son.
By faith Isaac blessed Jacob and Esau concerning things to come.
By faith Joseph, when he died, made mention of the deliverance of the children of Israel, and gave commandment concerning his bones.
By faith Moses refused to be called the son of Pharaoh's daughter, choosing rather to suffer affliction with the people of God.
By faith the walls of Jericho fell down. By faith Rahab perished not with them that believed not.

And what shall I more say? For the time would fail me to tell of Gideon, and of Barak, and of Samson, and of Jephthah; of David also: who through faith—

Subdued kingdoms
Wrought righteousness
Stopped the mouths of lions
Quenched the violence of fire
Escaped the edge of the sword
Out of weakness were made strong
Waxed valiant in fight
Turned to flight the armies of the aliens.

Others were tortured—

They were stoned
They were sawn asunder
Were tempted, were slain with the sword.
They wandered about in sheepskins and goatskins
Being destitute, afflicted, tormented.
They wandered in deserts
And in mountains
And in dens and caves of the earth.

Of Whom the World Was Not Worthy.

Wherefore seeing we are compassed about with so great a cloud of witnesses, let us run with patience the race that is set before us. So that we (also) may boldly say:

The Lord is my helper,
I will not fear
What man shall do unto me.

Arranged from HEBREWS, 11.

PART I

IN THE BEGINNING—MAN

THE COOL OF THE DAY

And God said, "Let us make man in our image."

So God created man in his own image, in the image of God created he him.

And the Lord God planted a garden eastward in Eden; and there he put the man whom he had formed. And out of the ground made the Lord God to grow every tree that is pleasant to the sight, and good for food; the tree of life also in the midst of the garden, and the tree of knowledge of good and evil.

And the Lord God took the man, and put him into the garden of Eden to dress it and to keep it. And the Lord God commanded the man, saying, "Of every tree of the garden thou mayest freely eat: but of the tree of the knowledge of good and evil, thou shalt not eat."

And the Lord God caused a deep sleep to fall upon Adam, and he slept: and he took one of his ribs. And the rib, which the Lord God had taken from man, made he a woman, and brought her unto the man.

And Adam called his wife's name Eve. . . . And they were both naked, the man and his wife, and were not ashamed.

From GENESIS 1, 2, & 3

WHO WAS whispering in the garden? Eve, in the middle of the Garden of Eden, looked about her quietly amused. Adam was sleeping under the tree of the knowledge of good and evil—Adam must be whispering in his sleep. Eve, smiling to herself, stole toward Adam.

But it wasn't Adam who was whispering, Adam was sleeping quietly. Under the tree nice, sweet, innocent Eve stood head tilted to determine where the whispers were coming from. It was a sly whispering, as if someone were whispering to himself an amusing secret that he knew and that Eve didn't know. But it wasn't Adam.

It was a serpent. Eve looked up into the tree of the knowledge of good and evil—a serpent was whispering up in the tree. Eve stood head tilted back, amused and intrigued by the serpent's sly whispering and the sly flick of his eyes with which he looked down at her from the bough.

In ecstasy the serpent rubbed his flattened head against the beautiful fruit of the tree. "Did God tell you," he whispered dreamily, "that you might not eat of the fruit of this tree? But look at the beautiful fruit!"

"Oh, no," Eve said, aghast. "We may eat of every tree in the garden, but God said if we ate of this tree we would die."

"Die?" the serpent said. "Die? God told you that? You won't die! You'll see—the moment you eat of this fruit your eyes will be opened—then, like me, you'll really see how beautiful this fruit is! The most beautiful in the whole garden. And so good to eat!"

Eve looked up at the fruit.

"Shall I tell you a secret?" the serpent whispered. He rubbed his head against the fruit. "I'll tell you a secret that only God and I know. But you'll know it, too, when you eat the fruit of this tree of the knowledge of good and evil. You'll see—then you'll know both good and evil, too—just like God! It's as simple as that. God knows both good and evil, but all you know is good. But as soon as you eat from this tree, you'll know good and evil, then you'll be just like God. Why, don't you see—you'll be one of the gods. You'll be a goddess, Eve!"

Simple Eve was impressed. What a wise serpent! It must be good to be wise like the serpent.

The serpent was silent, but his eyes flickered knowingly.

Eve's hand went up into the tree. Eve pulled down one of the beautiful fruits. Eve bit into it. As Eve bit into the fruit, her eyes were opened, just as the serpent had said. But now Eve did not look up at the serpent, instead she looked in horror and shame at Adam lying under the tree. Adam was naked. There he lay, and he was naked! Eve gasped and Adam awoke.

Adam was no different from what he had been before, but Eve had not known what nakedness meant. Now she was ashamed and horrified. She backed away from the naked Adam—it was shameful, awful; it was indecent. Suddenly she rushed back to Adam, and thrust the fruit at him—the fruit she had taken from the tree, and from which she had taken one bite.

The wondering Adam also took a bite. But as Adam bit into the fruit, his eyes opened, his eyes, too, jumped wide. And Adam looked at Eve, and Adam said, "You're naked!"

Eve nodded tearfully. She guiltily tugged some leaves from the tree to cover herself. But then she ran, she rushed away from Adam, because she wasn't innocent any more—she was naked.

It was in the cool of the evening, at the dawn of creation, in the Garden of Eden. Adam and Eve, the first man and first woman, were hidden in the Garden. But they had not hid together. Adam had hid under low, shadowing trees, Eve had thrown herself down in the deep grass among thick bushes. They had hid, each one apart, for they were guilty and they were naked.

Then the voice of God came into the Garden. The little leaves shook at the sound of the great voice of God. And God said, "Adam, where are you?"

Adam knew that he should run out to God as he always had run out to God before, but he could not. He looked down at himself. Even with the little apron of leaves he had wreathed for himself, he still felt so naked that he dared not go out to God. But he had to answer God. He cast down his eyes, and called out in a guilty voice, "I didn't do it. Eve—the woman you gave me—did it. She did it! She ate of the fruit of the forbidden tree. And then I ate. And now, oh, Lord God, I can't come out to you, because I am naked."

Among the bushes Eve cringed at what she heard Adam say to God. With hasty, guilty fingers she tried to finish the apron of leaves she had been trying to make for herself, so that she, too, could run out to God as she always had run out to God before. But her fingers weren't willing, and the leaves wouldn't shape, and Eve cried out to God from among the thick bushes, "I didn't do it. I didn't. The snake did it! The snake told me to take some of the fruit from the forbidden tree, and I did, and I ate, and I gave some to Adam. And Adam ate it, too!"

But the snake was silent.

The voice of God came through the Garden, and the voice of God was so sorrowful, the little leaves shook. "Because you did this," God told the woman and the man, "the one thing, the only thing, I forbade you to do—now I will have to cast you out from the Garden forever. Forever to live among weeds and thorns, among sickness and sin, and sorrow and death. Always to live among struggle and strife—struggle and strife."

Then the voice of God was gone from the Garden. But it was so sad, and the first man and first woman felt so pitifully naked and guilty, God left some clothes made from animal skins for them in the Garden.

In the cool of the evening Adam and Eve, clothed in the new animal skins God had given them, left the beautiful Garden of Eden. The Garden was so still that Adam and Eve could hear the slight rustle their clothes of new hides made as they walked from the Garden; they felt the rub of the animal skins against their own skins that had never felt clothes before. Stooped, guilty, and shamed, the man and the woman rustled away in their new skins and left the perfect Garden of Eden forever. And when from far away they hopelessly looked back, there was the flaming light of an angel guarding the entrance to Eden with a flaming sword to prevent the two people from ever entering the perfect Garden again.

In the Garden itself in the cool of the evening there was another rustle, a very small rustle down in the grass, for now the serpent, too—all his harm done—left the Garden of Eden forever.

After the snake was gone, the Garden lay still, empty and still. And it was in the cool of the day, at the dawn of creation, and the perfect Garden of Eden lay empty and still.

STRUGGLE AND STRIFE

And Adam called his wife's name Eve; because she was the mother of all living. . . . And Eve bore Cain, and said, "I have gotten a man from the Lord." And she again bore his brother Abel.

And Abel was a keeper of sheep, but Cain was a tiller of the ground. And in process of time it came to pass that Cain brought of the fruit of the ground an offering unto the Lord. And Abel, he also brought of the firstlings of his flock and of the fat thereof. And the Lord had respect unto Abel and to his offering: but unto Cain and his offering he had not respect.

And Cain was very wroth. . . .

From GENESIS 3 & 4

THE FIRST child born in the world—Eve's first baby—was Cain. There sat Eve before the mud hut that Adam had built for her on the world's first stony, thorny farm, and she cradled in her lap the world's first living child. And Eve—looking up from the stones and the land, looking up from the baby in her lap, looking up to God in the evening stillness—suddenly picked up her child and held him high, as if holding him up to God, and in her triumph she jubilated, "He is Cain. His name is Cain, for I have gotten a man from the Lord."

At Eve's cry of triumph in the evening stillness, Adam, grubbing with a heavy hoe in a stony corner of the field, straightened his stooped back and looked at Eve. But Eve sat humble and quiet before the hut again, looking at her baby in her lap again, for this was a wonder and a miracle—this her first child. Adam wiped the sweat from his eyes, and once more began grubbing away at the big stones in the field. And now Eve watched Adam at his heavy work.

This, Eve knew, was their punishment for eating from the forbidden tree in the Garden of Eden. It had come about exactly as God had said: "Cursed is the ground, thorns and thistles shall it bring forth; in the sweat of your face you shall eat your bread."

Ah, God had promised nothing but struggle and strife, and the struggle had begun. But as Eve looked from Adam to the child in her lap, it seemed to her that the coming of her child, the first living child, almost made the struggle worth-while, sweetened it with the loveliness of a perfect miracle.

Time went on, and Eve had another son—Abel—a gentle, quiet lad.

Time went on, and it seemed long ago—terribly, wearily long ago—from that awful day at the dawn of creation when Adam and Eve, stooped, hurried, and shamed, had rushed away from the perfect Garden of Eden. Oh, long ago. Cain and Abel had grown up. There were other children, and the little mud hut at the end of the field had grown more rooms as Adam and Eve had more sons and daughters.

Abel grew up gentle and quiet and devout. He tended the flock, and almost daily—as his mother Eve had taught him when he was a child—he offered a sacrifice to God from his flock. Nearly every evening in the corner of the field where the stones were piled, the smoke from Abel's offering rose in a thin, tall column up to heaven—an offering to the God of creation.

Cain, when he remembered it, also made offerings to God. But often he forgot, he was so busy tilling the soil and raising the crops and clearing the field of the stones that forever kept cropping up. It seemed all on his shoulders—Adam was getting too old for the heavy work of clearing the land—strain each heavy boulder up above the knees, hoist and tug it up, hug the stone against the stomach, lug the heavy thing to the corner of the field. Yes, it seemed all on his shoulders—Abel had an easy time of it, tending gentle sheep. He had time for making an altar from the stone pile, time for evening sacrifice—he wasn't very tired from tending sheep.

Now this evening again—there the smoke of Abel's sacrifice rose in a straight column over the trees, before it feathered and plumed out over the field where Cain still grubbed a stone out of the ground. It smelled sweet—good meat, good fat. And Cain remembered that he had not sacrificed for a whole week. Now at the lovely odors of the broiling meat, he dropped the huge stone he had been hoisting to his knees, grabbed a handful of wheat, snatched up another handful, added some lentils, and then still tugged up a few turnips, weeds and all. He felt the prickle of the thistles in the palm of his hand as he hurried with his tight handful to Abel's smoking offering on the stone pile in the corner of the field. He didn't take time to sort out the thistles and weeds, but threw the whole wet handful on top of Abel's offering—it saved the long, slow work of starting a fire.

Wet and limp the greens slumped over the fire and choked it. The sweet smoke of the broiling meat changed into a smelly smudge. The smudge didn't rise into the evening air, but lay low around the stone pile; the stench and the smudge crawled over the ground. Cain stood at the rock pile choking and coughing in the heavy smoke that wrapped itself around him.

Abel must still have been somewhere near. Abel must have smelled the smudge. Abel came running. "Cain, what are you doing? What have you done to my sacrifice?"

Abel plunged into the smoke, tried to snatch away the limp, wet mess that drooped over his offering of sweet young lamb.

"Don't you touch it," Cain said savagely. He stepped into the smoke. Teary-eyed he glared at Abel, blindly grabbed at his brother. Abel eluded him, and once more tried to snatch away the limp, smelly, weedy mess.

"I said don't!" Cain grabbed blindly at his brother to hurl him away from the altar. Somehow he grabbed Abel by the throat, then he was savagely choking Abel. And before he knew what he had done, Cain felt Abel go limp in his hands. And then there was death—the world's first death. Abel was dead.

Cain looked at his hands, looked at his slumped brother, and then Cain knew fear. He had killed his brother! Strife had come among men, and out of the strife had come death. Abel was dead.

Now there was nothing he—Cain—could do, and nothing that he could undo. All Cain could do—all he could think to do—was to run. He ran wildly, madly away from the stone pile. Away across the fields, away from the farm of his father Adam and the hut of his mother Eve. Away from his brothers and sisters, and from all living men, because he had killed a man. He lunged away. He threw himself ahead across the fields. He scattered the frightened flock of his brother Abel before him. The sheep of Abel, who was dead.

In a far field the voice of God came running after Cain. There came the voice of God. It stopped Cain dead in the middle of a field. It turned him to stone. Then in the stillness of the evening field the voice of God asked Cain, "Where is your brother Abel?"

And Cain stood half turned away from the voice of God, and sullen with fear he snarled up to God, "How should I know? Am I my brother's keeper?"

But God knew. And Cain knew that God knew. The sullen, snarling coward, the murderer, became a cowering wretch. On hands and knees he tried to crawl away from the voice of God. He sniveled up to God, "I did it. I did it! Now everyone will hunt me, and when they find me they will kill me, too."

The words came screaming, hiccoughing out of him, jerky with his crawling.

Amazingly, the pity of God went out to the sobbing murderer. God had pity. God said to the crawling wretch, "I will save you from the vengeance of man. I will brand you, so that everyone that finds you will know that, if they harm you, they will be punished sevenfold."

In the darkening evening field suddenly seven ugly marks —marks like scars—appeared on the forehead of the crawl-

ing Cain. It was the sevenfold mark of the sevenfold vengeance of God on whoever should seek to kill Cain. Then God and the voice of God were gone from the evening field.

Alone, and with his forehead seared and branded, Cain stumbled up and ran again. Alone he fled to the land of Nod. There he settled in that lonely land to till for himself a little piece of stony soil. There he lived alone—a haunted, branded man, who could never forget his brother.

But it happened in the course of time—there in the lonely, harsh land of Nod, where Cain had built his small hut—that a woman came along. And the woman took pity on Cain. She did not flee from the terrible sevenfold brand on the forehead of the silent man. She did not shudder away—she had pity, even as God had taken pity on this miserable man. Pity became love, and the woman became Cain's wife, and they had children. And the years rolled on, and the generations.

THE QUIET ONE

And Enoch lived sixty and five years, and begat Methuselah:

And Enoch walked with God after he begat Methuselah three hundred years, and begat sons and daughters.

And all the days of Enoch were three hundred sixty and five years:

And Enoch walked with God: and he *was* not; for God took him.

And it came to pass when men began to multiply on the face of the earth, and daughters were born unto them, that the sons of God saw the daughters of men that they were fair; and they took them wives of all which they chose.

There were giants in the earth in those days; and also after that, when the sons of God came in unto the daughters of men, and they bare children to them, the same became mighty men which were of old men of renown.

And God saw that the wickedness of man was great in the earth.

From GENESIS 5 & 6

ADAM was still living, but Adam was old—centuries old. The man who had once been perfect, who had lived in the perfect Garden of Eden, and who had walked and talked with God in the cool of the day in the Garden of Eden, lived on and on for over nine hundred years. Adam, the first man, lived on among his multiplying descendants—among his children, grandchildren, and great-grandchildren—yes, even among his great, great, great, great, great-grandchildren. To old Adam it often must have seemed that as men multiplied, wickedness multiplied—wickedness and strife and murder and hate—the wickedness that had begun with his own son, Cain. Ah, the perfect life in the perfect Garden was centuries away.

Cain, the murderer, Adam's first son, also lived on through the centuries, and Cain's descendants multiplied—but also Cain's sin. There was murder, and hate, and struggle, and strife in the little world of man, even though the whole little world of man consisted of nothing but the village of Adam and the village of Cain. At the beginning, in those two early dawn villages, lived the whole race of man.

The village of Adam was not far from the perfect Garden of Eden. The village of Cain was in the land of Nod to the east of the Garden of Eden. Adam and Cain, each heading a village, lived on among their descendants, and the race of man grew in the earth. However, Cain's village was a village of wickedness, but in Adam's village, while Adam lived, men worshiped God. Men called upon the name of God.

In his village, Adam, the first man, the man who had been perfect—who had walked and talked with God—lived on among his descendants, and to Adam's descendants that must have been awesome to think about and to contemplate. But Adam was becoming very old, and somewhat decrepit.

Adam was centuries old when Enoch his great, great, great, great-grandson was born in his village. Enoch grew up, and Enoch was sixty-five years old when he himself had a son —Methusaleh, who was to become still older than Adam.

Methusaleh was to become the world's oldest man—nine hundred and sixty-nine years old.

But that lay in the future, and the coming centuries, and in the endless unknown—and all men lived long. What mattered now, as Enoch grew older, was that God came back to earth and man. God came back to the early dawn village of Adam to walk and talk with a man. It was a little as if the perfection of the Garden of Eden was coming back to man. But it did not come to Adam, who once had walked with God in the Garden. It was not to Adam that God returned—it was to Enoch.

To Enoch, the quiet one. For Enoch was the silent one, who lived and walked alone—as much as a father and head of a growing family could live alone. To be alone, and away from the busyness and hustle and bustle and loudness of village life—Enoch walked alone. Every evening he went into the fields and walked in the soft quiet that comes to fields in the eventide. In the cool of the day when work was done, in the stillness far afield that was like a holiness, Enoch walked alone.

Always Enoch walked far, and he only returned to the village after night had fallen. Not for him the loudness of talk and banter and boasting, and the gossip of the village square. But often, when Enoch returned to the village, the coldness of night would have fallen, and the men of the village would have built a fire for warmth and light, and to prolong the talk and the evening. Sometimes Enoch would join the men at the fire in the village square.

The villagers resented Enoch and his self-sufficient quietness. They resented it that he walked away from the village life every evening again when work was done. And sometimes when Enoch sat down with them at the fire they would question him. Why did he walk? Why alone? Where did he walk? And did he talk to himself when he walked alone? Or wasn't there ever a need in him for talk?

Enoch did not say. He might say a few quiet things about the work of the day and the work for tomorrow, and the crops, and the fields and the flocks, but he did not answer the questions. Ever the quiet, inscrutable one, he would sit by the fire to warm and rest himself, and after the few quiet words he would stare into the fire, and always his eyes seemed turned in on himself, and always his thoughts seemed far away. Soon he would leave and go to his house and bed.

The men would be relieved when Enoch left. For when Enoch was there the talk always died, the laughter left, and no one attempted banter or nonsense. What could you say to Enoch that did not sound foolish and vacant and empty and small? And certainly you never told the tales of the evil doings in the village of Cain—not when Enoch was there at the fire.

But this day—this evening—news came to the village fire, and from the fire it raced through the whole village. For once the news was not of the wicked doings in the village of Cain in the land of Nod—this night the news was about Enoch. The news was hustled to the men gathered around the fire in the village square by a young man just freshly returned out of the fields. He had gone to his sheep cote late in the evening to tend to a hurt lamb. All this time they'd supposed that Enoch walked alone, hadn't they? Enoch did not walk alone! Enoch had a companion. Somebody walked with Enoch in the evening fields. And Enoch must know him very well. They walked and talked as good friends walk and talk.

The young man had seen them walk close together far away across the fields. And the quiet Enoch had talked and talked; the young man had seen him gesture as a man does in earnest talk. Then the young man stunned all those around the fire by what he told them. It was God! Enoch walked with no man—Enoch walked with God!

No one laughed—they sat stunned. No one around the fire really believed, still they were awed. No one in the village could believe it. Then they took the news to old, old Adam, and Adam seemed to find no reason not to believe.

To Adam, who had walked and talked with God, to Adam who had been perfect, it seemed perfectly reasonable and believable—a little touch of Eden, a little of perfection, a little of holiness come back to earth, a little of nearness to God again. Adam nodded his white head, and mumbled words of gratitude and adoration. And the whole village believed—Adam believed it.

After that day no one dared question Enoch as to why he walked, and where he walked, and with whom he walked. But the villagers watched Enoch, and they took to following him at a great, respectful, frightened distance. Then they found a high hill that commanded a view in every direction of the wide, far fields.

And it was so! The young man had told the truth; Adam had rightly believed. Many evenings Enoch walked alone, but on some evenings at the most unexpected moment, somewhere in the fields, God joined Enoch in his walk. God was there—suddenly God was there, and the two walked on together. They walked and talked as good friends do, and the awed villagers looked on in reverence. Sometimes God and Enoch stopped in the fields, then they would walk on again, side by side, until the dusk gathered them from sight. And a holy stillness would lie over the fields with the coming of the night, until at last only one figure would emerge out of the darkness—Enoch walked back to the village alone.

Now every evening instead of gathering around a fire in the village square, the villagers watched on the hill. And on the evenings that God came to walk with Enoch the watchers would send word, and the whole village would gather on the high hill. Afterward a few of them would always faithfully visit old Adam to tell him all that they had seen.

This silent night the word came late—Enoch was with God. The village emptied, the people hurried to the top of the hill. Enoch and God walked far away, but the field was visible where the two figures moved. Adam had asked it, and this night the villagers brought Adam to the hill. They carried him up the hill on a litter. They stood him up on his feet and held him up. The night was clear with stars and moonlight. They pointed out to Adam the two figures moving far away, and even Adam with age-dimmed eyes could see. Adam looked long, he nodded and nodded as he looked, and then he bowed his head in silent reverence. Old and decrepit as he was, he kneeled. All looked at Adam. All the questioning eyes asked Adam—was it so? Was it God? He who knew, he who had also walked and talked with God—was it God? Adam said it softly. "It is God."

Then they all kneeled with Adam. They whispered it over the hill. "It is God."

A few years—as the years were reckoned when men lived for centuries—after his visit to the hill, Adam died. Nine hundred and thirty years old, Adam died. Gone from the village of his descendants was Adam, the first man, who had once been perfect. The first man who had walked and talked with God. Then there was only Enoch.

It was enough. For still through the years and the centuries, awed by Enoch and his nearness to God, the villagers worshiped and called on the name of God. And through the years—still always awed—they kept watching Enoch walk with God through the evening fields in a stillness of peace and of holiness. Nightly there were watchers on the hill.

But one still evening came word to the village, so awesome, so crushing, so final, that everyone rushed to the hill. And the word was that Enoch was no more. God had taken him. The few watchers on the hill had seen it—no, they had not really seen anything happen at all. As always before, Enoch had walked through the fields with God, but the next moment Enoch had been no more.

There was no mistaking it, as all the villagers looked on. Only one walked away over the fields into the gathering dusk—and it was God. God walked alone. There was no Enoch.

Long the villagers stood on top of the hill, long after God had walked away into the gathering dusk and stillness. They waited until God was gone, then they all rushed to the spot where Enoch had disappeared. They found the spot the early watcher indicated was the exact spot of Enoch's disappearance. But they found no sign, not a mark, not the scrape of the sole of a foot, and not a bent grass. But it must be the spot. The double trail of bent grasses that feet had trodden led to the spot—a single trail of bent grasses where God had walked on alone led from the spot. Silently the villagers returned to their village. No one uttered a word. They could not have put it in words, but it was as if a little bit of holiness had left the earth. It was as if a little of the perfection and stillness of holiness that had come back to earth with Enoch was gone forever.

It did not happen immediately. Long the village of Adam and Enoch stayed awed and reverent. But the years rolled on. No longer did Enoch walk with God. No longer did the villagers watch from the hill. No longer did the stillness of holiness seem to lie all around. It was as if, God having withdrawn from the earth, Adam gone and Enoch gone—the two who had walked and talked with God—the children of men left behind on the earth in the two villages drew closer together. The two villages, the village of Cain, and the village of Adam. It was as if wickedness moved into the village of Adam.

The fire was built again in the village square. Men gathered around the fire in the evening after work was done to talk loud and laugh loud, and to gossip. Nightly around the

fire lurid tales were told of doings of wickedness in the village of Cain. The talk about the village of Cain seemed to interest the men of the village of Adam every evening and every evening again. But from telling of tales of wickedness men became interested in the wickedness, and from the village of Adam men began to visit the village of Cain in the land of Nod.

One night tall news was told around the fire, and it was rushed through the whole village of Adam—a young man from the village was marrying a girl from the village of Cain! As men talked and talked late that night, it was told and understood that many of the young men of the village had taken up with the young women of the village of Cain. And as it was talked about, it was deemed good—now the small race of man would multiply much faster in the earth. And at the fire that night a man even dared to prophesy that some day the race of man would fill the earth.

There was great talk. But no one seemed to notice or understand that as the two early dawn villages mixed and intermingled, and men multiplied, that wickedness also multiplied. And, as wickedness grew, strife and struggle and confusion grew. The stillness of holiness was far from the earth. And few there were that walked with God.

PART II

A NEW BEGINNING OF MAN

THE PREACHING OF NOAH

And God saw that the wickedness of man was great in the earth, and that every imagination of the thoughts of his heart was only evil continually. And it repented the Lord that he had made man on the earth.

And the Lord said, "I will destroy man whom I have created from the face of the earth; both man, and beast, and the creeping thing, and the fowls of the air; for it repenteth me that I have made them."

But Noah found grace in the eyes of the Lord.

And God said unto Noah, "The end of all flesh is come before me. . . . Make thee an ark of gopherwood."

From GENESIS 6

IT DIDN'T make sense. It didn't begin to make sense. Now there it started again, the hammering and pounding. All the rest of the village was still at supper, resting from the day's work, but that man, Noah, didn't know what rest was. There he was pounding away at that ark again. The man was driven. He was possessed. He was a fool.

In the village the people around their supper tables glanced up at the sound of the pounding, started to shake their heads, went on eating. They had long since run out of jokes about Noah. All the funny remarks were not funny any more—all the tired old jokes. But they actually would have felt let down if the pounding hadn't begun at supper time. How long had it been now? How many years had that man sawed and hammered and pounded on that boat? Altogether too many to think up anything new to say about it. After supper—if they felt like it—the men would wander around to the edge of the village and stand with the other men watching Noah build the ark. It was something to do until darkness fell.

They ought to put a stop to it. The watchers and loafers agreed on that again this evening, just as they agreed on it every evening. It ought to be stopped. The whole village was becoming notorious—all on account of Noah. The village was becoming a laughingstock—people were coming from miles around to see Noah's boat. . . . Well, they did get to see some new faces that way, and hear some news from the rest of the world. But just the same they were getting to feel awfully foolish and silly trying to explain Noah's foolishness to the visitors.

"A boat?" every stranger would be sure to say. "Is he building a real boat that's supposed to float? Out here?"

"Yes, he's building a real boat on dry land," the villagers would constantly have to tell them. Then the visitors would look as if the villagers had gone crazy, too.

But one thing could be said for Noah—even if he was building a boat on dry land, and for nothing, he surely must be building the world's biggest boat. . . . Here in the flatlands, the dry, corky flatlands—building a boat four hundred and fifty feet long and as wide as a river. It was miles from any river, miles from the sea, but at least it was as wide as a river.

Noah was building his boat three stories high! It towered above the whole village. It loomed dark and huge in the flatlands. It could be seen for miles, and people did come from miles away to see. But this rainy evening there were no visitors, no strangers, and no information to give out to them about Noah's ark. The men of the village stared resentfully at the looming boat—in a way they were secretly proud of the notoriety Noah had brought to the dull village. It brought strangers and talk and news. But tonight not a soul.

The men stood in the misting rain, silent, talked out, bored. Now out of his boredom one of the jokers yelled up to Noah, "It's going fine, Noah. Another century and you ought to be done. It's just too bad though that you started it wrong—if you'd only put wheels under it."

From the three-story-high boat, Noah looked down on the men for a moment, a brooding, silent look.

"Don't stop, Noah," another village wit yelled up. "You just get on with it—can't do much about the bottom now any more, so you just make it higher. Just build it up—that's the only place you can go with it anyway."

Noah did not answer, went on in silence, except for his hammering and sawing and pounding. If he was possessed, as the villagers continually told him, he was possessed of his faith in his Lord. The zeal of the Lord God of hosts possessed him—the Lord God who had told him to build an ark, and to make it of gopherwood, four hundred and fifty feet long, seventy-five feet wide, three stories high. With a small window in the top, and a big door in the side—a wide door, a high door. Wide enough for two elephants, high enough for giraffes.

The Lord had ordered it. Noah was building it as the years went on—he and his three sons. It was all his sons knew—they had grown up with the growing ark. Even as little toddlers they had helped their father, bringing him pieces of wood he couldn't use, getting underfoot, climbing up where they shouldn't. Through the growing years it had so become part of their lives; now it was a matter of course that Shem and Ham helped their father build the ark in the evenings after work. Not for them the lolling and loafing and swapping stories and eyeing the girls that paraded and circled the village square.

Shem and Ham—the urgency of their father had transferred to his two oldest sons. But no one else would help with the ark. The villagers wouldn't lift a finger to aid in the insanity—a boat on dry land! And the hints were strong and continual that after the ark was finished—if it ever got finished—that that's all it might be good for—to lock Noah and his whole crazy family into his dry-land boat.

Noah had long ago given up pleading, preaching, persuading. No longer did he tell them of the flood that God had told him would come. He no longer wasted the useless words. But he was still preaching, if they only knew. He was preaching with his hammer. The preaching of Noah was in the sound of his hammer, and his faith in God sounded out over the village and the flat countryside with each new peg he drove into the planks of gopherwood. But it was heart-rending that each plank, each peg, each brush smear of pitch brought the flood closer, brought doom nearer. They wouldn't believe.

They would only act knowing and wise, laugh and crack jokes. And Noah could only go on. God had ordered it.

Shem and Ham had learned from their father to go their own way in spite of what the crowd thought. And when it came time to marry, Shem and Ham had somehow found themselves wives. Of course, in those times the ark had not been so big, so high. Now it towered over the countryside. Everybody knew about Noah's foolish ark.

It was hard on Japheth, his youngest son. Noah knew it full well. One evening each week—courting evening—he let Japheth off from working on the ark to stand in the village square with the swains of the village, watching the girls circle and parade, until dusk came and the time to pair off with the girls. But Japheth did not pair off with a girl. Japheth came home alone. No girl wanted to be seen with him. Who wanted to be a laughingstock? Who wanted to be married to a laughingstock? Ah, Noah understood it too well.

Now the evening of this week it was courting evening in the village again. There was no rain. It would be a beautiful evening for courting. But at the supper table Japheth had sat staring hatefully at his food. "Come on, eat, son," his mother had said.

But Japheth had jumped up, thrown his chair back and jumped up, and choking and pointing at the dark window he'd burst out, "Who wants to eat? Who can eat? Everything is pitch. Everything smells like pitch, everything tastes like pitch, I can't even see my food for pitch!"

It was true enough. Outside the one window of the room

the ark rose beside the house. The pitch-smeared wall of the ark loomed black and somber, darkened the window, darkened the house, and everything reeked of pitch.

Noah had been hurrying out after his hasty supper to work on the ark, but he turned back and laid a hand on Japheth's unwilling shoulder. "I know how it is, son. I understand. But remember this, the ark won't float and the flood won't come until you, too, have a wife. I know it from the Lord—your mother and I, your brothers and their wives, and you and your wife will be on that ark. And then the flood will come."

But Japheth had glared down at his food and said nothing.

Now Shem and Ham were coming from the house, their supper finished, to help their father with the ark. Already a small group of loafers was gathering, and already the first wagon with curiosity seekers from outside was rolling toward the village. Shem and Ham had long ago learned—they walked silently by the group of loafers, not hearing the remarks, certainly not making any answer. As on all the many endless evenings they climbed up on the ark, picked up their hammers, and began.

The wagon drew up. The oxen halted. The farmer on the wagon sat silently looking up at the high strange structure of the ark. The girl beside him on the seat kept turning to him, kept asking him questions. One of the loafers yelled out a so-called joke to them. They didn't seem to hear. The girl was pointing at the great door of the ark and asking her father a question. He studied the enormous door in the side of the ark.

It was courting evening in the village, it was Japheth's

evening off, but there came Japheth now, too. He hadn't dressed in his evening best. He evidently wasn't going to the village square; he must have had enough of rebuffs.

In pitch-smeared clothes he squeezed his way through the group of idlers. They said sneering things to him, and suddenly he twisted his head and shot something back. The loafers all laughed and looked up at Noah on the roof of the ark. Noah's face darkened—the fools could make jokes about the ark, but his own son shouldn't. He hadn't asked Japheth to come spread pitch this evening. He was coming of his own free will. Now Japheth was passing the wagon without glancing at it. But when he had passed it, he turned and looked up as if surprised nobody had called some smart thing after him from the wagon. "Well, say it," he dared. His sullen face burned.

"Say what, son?" the farmer said. "That is really a tremendous undertaking. Do you work on it, too?"

"I smear pitch," Japheth said shortly.

But the girl had climbed down from the wagon. Now she pointed up at the little boatswain's swing, with the pot of pitch still hanging from it, dangling high against the side of the ark. "Do you work way up there—in that little swing?"

"Somebody has to sling pitch."

"Yes, but to dangle there from a rope—it looks dangerous, and exciting."

Noah looked down over the edge of the roof. Japheth looked at the girl—she wasn't laughing, she was asking serious questions. Japheth began explaining things to her; the girl was listening, and not laughing. The farmer called out a question to them. They didn't hear, walked on. The farmer climbed down from the wagon and hurried after them. The three disappeared into the ark, and Noah got busy on the roof.

Now at last the wagon lumbered away behind the plodding oxen; the girl sat turned on the seat waving up at the ark. She seemed to be waving at Noah. Noah started to wave back, but then he peered over the edge of the roof. Japheth was just below him, back in the boatswain's swing, dangling from the rope, waving his pitch brush to the girl. He was whistling.

Noah couldn't quite resist. "It's fine to have the mind on the girl, but keep your eyes on the pitch—we can't have even one leaky spot."

Japheth made a threatening gesture with a brushful of pitch, and grinned up at his father.

"Not going to the village square?" Noah asked too innocently.

"Me? No! I just spread pitch."

"Yes, I heard you spreading it to that girl—quite an authority on arks and pitch, aren't you?"

"Oh, I know my pitch."

And Noah and his son could grin and joke together—because a girl hadn't laughed. And the work went on.

The work went on every evening, and every evening again. It was interrupted only for the night of Japheth's wedding. It was a quiet little family affair. None of the villagers had come, none had been invited. The separation between the village and the family of Noah was complete. The ark was being finished. Even the girl's father had not come—he had died months before.

There were only the four men and their wives, all of them in one house, with an ark looming over it. It was good for the wives of the sons of Noah to live together that way with their mother-in-law. No one else would have much of anything to do with them. They, too, were a laughingstock. The silly women were the wives of the crew of a dry-land boat.

DEEP WATER

And the Lord said unto Noah, "Come thou and all thy house into the ark; for thee have I seen righteous before me in this generation. Of every clean beast thou shalt take to thee by sevens, the male and his female: and of beasts that are not clean by two, the male and his female. Of fowls also of the air by sevens, the male and the female; to keep seed alive upon the face of all the earth. For yet seven days, and I will cause it to rain upon all the earth forty days and forty nights; and every living substance that I have made will I destroy from off the face of the earth."

And Noah did according unto all that the Lord commanded him.

From GENESIS 7: 1-5

THE rain came. Rain? Well, hardly that—now for a week it had been little more than a misting, little more than the clouds hanging low over the flat land. Day after day of fog; dark, heavy days in the village. Mists curtained the streets, fog dulled the pitch-shiny ark. The towering ark dripped with dampness, but the great door—wide enough for two elephants, tall enough for giraffes—stood wide open in the wet and misery and dampness, as if something, many things, had to come in.

The family of Noah had moved into the ark—the whole insane crew of eight. Now, the villagers said among themselves, somebody ought to close the big door of the ark and nail it shut. With the whole crew inside. Eight people had gone to live in a four hundred and fifty feet long, three-story high boat. On dry land! Did they expect the big clumsy mass of lumber would float away on the mists? Wasn't this the way the rainy season always started—mists and clouds and damp, and then the rains came? But that was the way the seasons worked in their turn—summer then winter, seedtime then harvest, cold then heat. . . . But there those fools sat in their damp ark with the door wide open in the mists.

At least, the villagers told each other, it seemed a comfort not to hear the dreary pounding any more, evening after evening, and into the nights. . . . But through the little windows of their houses the women of the village kept watching the silent, dripping, wide-open doorway of the ark. The women were endlessly curious. In the evenings when the husbands came home from work in the fields, they were given a full report.

This evening the women reported, "The door's still open. But now they've emptied the house completely. They've moved lock, stock, and barrel into the ark."

That was the report on the first evening of the misty week. But on the third day there came a strangeness, an anxiety, into the reports of the women. The husbands coming home from the fields that night found the doors barred; the women had locked themselves and the children inside the houses. As they timidly let their husbands in out of the wet, they pleaded with them not to go out to the fields tomorrow—to stay home with them and the children.

According to the women, things had begun to happen about an hour before the men came home. Even at that early hour, because of the mist and fog, the village street had already lain in pale night darkness. The mist hid and concealed almost everything—still the women were sure. Down the village street, quiet and in order, silent and orderly, had come troops of animals—tame and wild animals, all mixed. Mind you—the women swore it to the laughing men—there'd been cows and pigs and antelopes, all mixed. But then—the men could believe it or not—there'd come a flock of lambs, sweet and young and out of season—lambs weren't born this time of year. . . . But behind the seven lambs had come two lions, and, walking right between the lions, keeping measured step with them, two tigers and two black leopards!

Those fierce wild animals hadn't touched the lambs, and the lambs hadn't been afraid. The lambs had all but gone dancing up the ramp into the ark, the lions and the tigers trudging steadily on behind them. Those two fierce leopards had shown no more interest in the lambs than if the black leopards had been black oxen. They hadn't come back. Everything that went into the ark stayed in the ark.

"Down the street, eh? Right down the street?"

"Oh, please," the women pleaded with their men. "Don't stand there grinning. Of course, there isn't anything in the street now but they came right down that street!"

But the strange animals, the likes of which they had never seen before, hadn't only come down the village street, they'd come from every direction toward the ark. Some across fields, some flying, some down the street.

"Look! Look, now!" The women rubbed at their bleak,

mist-dampened windows. Had it begun again? Couldn't they see it—movement going on there at the edge of the village—there at the great yawning doorway of the ark?

Aw, said the men, it was only the lifting and falling of the mist. You could make any kind of shapes out of the movement of fog—if you were scared enough. Just shrouds and wisps of pluming fog and mist. What really could you see against the wall of a pitch-black ark looming up out of mist?

That night the men did not laugh quite so loudly—and the men did not go out into the night to investigate. The black movement of things seemed to go on in the black of night. Not a thing could be seen from the tiny windows, but there was a feel, a sense of motion in the street, of things slithering, creeping, moving silently toward the ark.

Then at midnight a wild, possessed scream rang out in the village street—an eerie sound that belonged only in jungles. It scared people awake, scared them out of their beds, but there was nothing to be seen. Ah, it must only be jackals calling out in the open fields. Sure! A jackal could scream from miles away and make it sound as if he were under your bed. In the night you were scared and imagined things.

In the morning there was nothing. Nothing but the silent ark, and the wide-open door, and the empty ramp as wide as the doorway. The men went out to their work in the fields to finish their farm work before the big rains came. But the men waited for each other, and they went in groups. While in the village they talked and joked loudly to each other, but that was for the sake of the women and children. Along the road they talked seriously amongst themselves, comparing notes of what they had seen, or thought they had heard and seen in the night. They came to one grim conclusion—it had to be stopped. They'd waited far too long, they should have stopped Noah long ago. Something had to be done, because this was magic, black, hellish magic. That Noah was not only insane, he was a magician of the deepest, blackest sort, practicing magic as black as the pitch on his ark, as black as the nethermost regions of hell.

But was it so? Was what the women had seen, and what they themselves had thought they had heard and seen, really so? Was Noah with his magic filling the ark with the wildest and fiercest of wild beasts such as never before had been seen in this part of the world? Or was it fear that made them see things in the night? Could it be only mists and shadows and scared night imaginings? But you didn't build an ark four hundred and fifty feet long and three stories high just to house mists and shadows and eight people.

That day the mists rolling over the men in the fields changed to a drizzle, before the day was gone the drizzling changed to rain—the first steady droning rain of the wet season. But still it wasn't a downpour, it wasn't coming down by buckets, the way the rainy season usually started. "It's got to rain a little more than that, men, to float Noah's ark—especially if it's loaded with animals. . . . It wouldn't be bad if it did rain a little harder—just enough to float Noah away. . . ."

The jokes fell flat as if heavy with rain, for unseen in the blackness of rain there was a sound of wings above the men in the fields. Birds were flying in the rain. Enormous birds, enormous wings. They could hear the sighing whistle of the unseen wings. It must be true. It was not their imaginings. The birds, the wings were up there, for in one field out of the black and the invisibility a big white swan crashed into a tree, tumbled from the tree to the ground. Then his white mate, circling, came down, and the two swans huddled under the tree.

The men did not go out to the tree to club the helpless swan. They left. They called out the news to the men in other fields. They all left, for the rush of wings was above them everywhere, and the men hurried with bowed heads as if stooped under the weight of a sky filled with rain and wings. The women in the village silently unbarred the doors and silently let their men in.

Birds flew in a blackness of thundering rain by some horrible magic. But that seemed as nothing to the awfulness that came to the village street. In the middle of the afternoon an enormous tusked walrus heaved and threw himself forward over the streaming slippery roundness of the cobblestones. His tuskless mate flounced behind him, throwing herself ahead, clumsily trying to catch up. But a gaping crocodile slithered between them, scrabbled short-legged at the round cobblestones, pulling itself forward, toothed mouth wide agape and enormous with the enormous effort. And behind the tuskless walrus another crocodile slithered in the gushing wetness in the middle of the street.

Through the little windows the villagers looked at them, horrified. Stared from the crocodile going by to the end of

the village where the ark stirred. The ark had moved. The water was rising that high! The ark swayed, swung slightly away from the wall of Noah's house, lay still again. The water was rising, now the water animals, crocodiles, seals, walruses, snakes, unknown slithering, crawling things, were moving up the gushing ramp. The ark swung, and the great door stood wide open in the thundering rain.

In the night the rain lessened. Wasn't it always so? Hadn't it happened often before—water standing a foot deep in the streets in the rainy season in the village in the flat land? There'd be more rain, but now it was letting up. And if that ark swung much more, it was liable to knock Noah's house down—then he and his fool family'd have to live in that ark with their mad menagerie. People mumbled it to each other behind their little steamed windows, but they weren't convinced, didn't convince each other. Walruses in the street!

Now in the lessening rain and the lightening sky they could see the ark more plainly. They saw a pile of gopherwood planks drift away. There went a ladder! And now wasn't there activity in the doorway of the ark? Noah and Ham, Shem, and Japheth appeared in the doorway. The four stood looking at their ladders floating away, but they made no effort to retrieve them. And now Japheth mounted to Shem's shoulders and began smearing pitch around the huge door of the ark. They didn't bother about the ladders.

Now the three men dragged the great door nearly shut, and Japheth plastered pitch against it. Now Japheth smeared pitch into the grooved side of the doorway into which the door would slide. Now the door was open only a foot or so, and there was nothing moving into the ark. There were only the men, no animals, nothing slithering up the wet ramp. Suddenly all four men turned, stood looking out into the lessening rain. Just as suddenly they shoved the screaking door wide open again. They'd opened it just in time. A swan came flying, landed on top of the ramp in the doorway, and folded its wings. Noah stooped as if to pick up the swan, but the big white bird opened its wings and flew off again. The four men stood staring after it. They left the great door wide open, stood waiting.

Again the swan came, again it flew away. The water was rising. Even in the lessening rain the water kept rising as it came racing down from the distant mountains into the flat valley. The ark was lifting on the water. The ramp bobbled and swung. Still the door of the ark remained wide open, and still the men waited in the doorway.

There they came—not flying, swimming—the two swans on the deepening water. Close together, tight together. One must be the swan that had crashed into the tree and broken its wing. Now its mate swam beside it, tight against it, as if to hold up the poor, drooping wing. Together they swam to the foot of the bobbing ramp, together they clumsily walked up the ramp—tight together they went through the doorway. Then the great screaking door slid shut. And then there was a last pounding of the hammers as the door was pegged shut. Then the rain roared down. The people of the village peering anxiously from the windows saw nothing but sluicing, thunderous, awful rain. And while they couldn't see it surely, it seemed as if the ark was leaving them.

THE FOUNTAINS OF THE DEEP

And it came to pass after seven days that the waters of the flood were upon the earth.

In the second month, the seventeenth day of the month, the same day were all the fountains of the great deep broken up, and the windows of heaven were opened.

And the waters prevailed, and were increased greatly upon the earth; and the ark went upon the face of the waters.

And the waters prevailed exceedingly upon the earth. . . . And Noah only remained alive, and they that were with him in the ark.

And God remembered Noah, and every living thing, and all the cattle that was with him in the ark: and God made a wind to pass over the earth, and the waters assuaged.

The fountains also of the deep and the windows of heaven were stopped, and the rain from heaven was restrained.

And the waters returned from off the earth continually. . . .

And the ark rested in the seventh month, on the seventeenth day of the month, upon the mountains of Ararat.

From GENESIS 7 & 8

THE rain came down and the water came up. The rain came down and the water came up—forty days and forty nights. The windows of heaven seemed opened, and the rain came down the way waters of a great river roar down a waterfall. But it wasn't only the rain; the fountains of the deep opened up, came up, boiled up. The rain came down and the seas came up. The seas and the oceans came up in a great cold boiling to meet the water coming down from heaven. And in the great black boiling of water there was nothing else that moved but the pitch-black ark.

There was nothing else left under the sky. The hills had gone under in water. The water was lapping at the peaks of the mountains. Water was racing and roaring—not down—but up the mountains. And now there was nothing left but one peak of what must be the highest mountain. And nothing left on that peak, as the ark pitched toward it in the blackness and thunder of water, but a mountain goat. A cold, wet, bedraggled, hopeless mountain goat, four feet still planted around the point of the sharp, outcropping peak. The goat clung to the peak.

Noah peered from the ark's high window. The ark was roaring toward the peak of the mountain goat. There was nothing to be done. Nothing to stop the ark from crashing and ripping out its bottom on the jagged peak. But fast as the ark raced toward the peak, the water rose faster. Before the ark the peak went under and the goat went under and the ark raced safely over the peak of the highest mountain. Then all was gone from under the sky, and there was nothing but a pitch-black ark with a closed door and one small window, and now and then a face peering from the window, as the ark went heaving, racing, plunging on in an endlessness of rain. Forty days and forty nights. Rain, everlasting rain, endless water. And an ark floating helplessly over the mountains.

But after forty days and forty nights, as suddenly as it had begun, the awful rain stopped. A wind came into the rain, and then there was no more rain. Then there was no wind, and no rain. For days on end there was nothing but an awful stillness of water. No rain drumming, no water sluicing and roaring over the ark. Still it floated, still it drifted, and still the only sounds of life in all the earth were in the ark. But more and more the faces appeared in the window, as each one in turn, the four men and four women, would climb the ladder to the high window and look out longingly. Day after day, month after changeless month. Then after endless months a change suddenly came.

There, there! Out there and away. There, there it had appeared. Wasn't that a black peak? The bleak peak of a mountain? Land! Earth! A little sharp piece of the world. Rock! Glory be to God for that bit of rock. The water was going down, the earth was coming up. It was still there, after all the months and all the endless water—the good solid earth under the water.

After the lone bare peak had appeared to Noah and his family, there was always someone on top of the ladder at the high window as a lookout. They couldn't wait to see more of the earth, they couldn't bear to have any slight piece of earth appear, and they not see it. They hungered for land. And day by day, and little by little, more land came up from under the water. More mountain peaks came rising up, daily they rose a little higher. The slow, silent, cumbersome ark drifted and twirled among the mountain peaks.

Then one morning they awoke, and the ark floated and drifted and swung no more. It lay solid. They raced up the ladder, each one in turn, and each one in turn looked out of the window down on the mountain of Ararat on which the ark rested. The ark rested and drifted lonely no more. But below the peak of Ararat the water still stood threatening and still.

They opened the window. All the months it had been sealed tightly shut; now they broke it open. They needed to know if anywhere on earth beside the peak of Ararat there was a bit of land. Noah climbed to the open window with a raven—if the big black bird found a resting place . . . Noah thrust his hand far out of the window, opened his hand, and let the raven fly. The raven croaked away over the unearthly silence of endless water, the black wings flapped in the lonely sky. Noah watched the raven until it was a black dot, then even the dot was gone in the endlessness of sky over endless water.

They waited seven days for the raven to come back, but the raven did not return.

"It wasn't a good choice," Noah somberly told his family. "With all the carcasses still floating on the water! No, we shouldn't have picked a raven. He can ride the carcasses. It was a poor choice."

But wasn't that the croaking of a raven? Noah raced up the ladder to the window. Peered. There in the distance didn't something move? It was the raven! It came floating by on the bloated carcass of a mountain goat. The raven flapped its wings, and opened its gleaming yellow bill in a single hoarse croak, and dipped away on the mountain goat behind a ridge in the mountains.

"Bring up a dove—a white dove," Noah ordered. "A dove can't live on carcasses." His son, Shem, climbed up to him with a white dove. Noah stretched his hand out of the ark, and the dove whirred away across the water, but suddenly it wheeled and shot right through the open window back into the ark. Avoiding Noah's outstretched hand, it flew to a high beam, roosted high and out of reach. Noah looked at the dove and sighed. "She doesn't want to be caught and sent out into that again. Evidently there still is nothing but bare mountain rock. We'll have to wait."

They waited seven days. Then they caught the dove and sent her out again. Noah watched breathlessly as she whirred in a straight line farther and farther away, and out of sight. That day they stood all day around the ladder, but the dove did not come back. If nothing had happened to the dove, it was at least a hopeful sign, but the waiting was awful, and night was coming on. The sky was darkening; soon it would be night.

At the foot of the ladder the eight moped about in hopeless silence. It was so long, so long. Then up above them there was a whirring sound. Through the open window winged the dove, and in its beak it held a tiny twig with one tiny leaf. The dove dropped the leaf as it fluttered to its roost on the beam.

The little leaf fluttered down among the eight silent people. They just stared at it. At last Noah stooped and picked it up, peered at it in the half dark. "A little olive leaf," he stammered. "Somewhere life has come back on the earth. Somewhere things are growing—a little olive leaf, just unfolded."

The four women turned away and wept, and the four men turned away from each other, stood by themselves in unbelieving silence at this wondrous marvel of an olive leaf. Then from their places all turned to Noah at once—talking, wildly babbling, the words tumbling over each other. They passed the olive leaf from hand to hand, squeezed it between thumb and finger, asked for it back again—to feel it again. They looked up at the dove.

And suddenly, as he once more tenderly held the olive leaf, Noah shouted it out, shouted it loud for them all: "God gives us the earth back again. All the earth from an olive leaf. All the earth, all the wonderful, mighty, beautiful earth!"

And they kneeled and prayed.

SEEDTIME AND HARVEST

And God spake unto Noah, saying, "Go forth of the ark. . . ."

And Noah went forth, and his sons, and his wife, and his sons' wives with him.

Every beast, every creeping thing, and every fowl, and whatsoever creepeth upon the earth . . . went forth out of the ark.

And Noah builded an altar unto the Lord . . . and offered burnt offering on the altar.

And the Lord smelled a sweet savor; and the Lord said in his heart, "I will not again curse the ground any more for man's sake; for the imagination of man's heart is evil from his youth; neither will I again smite any more everything living, as I have done.

"While the earth remaineth, seedtime and harvest, and cold, and heat, and summer and winter, and day and night shall not cease."

From GENESIS 8

THERE stood the pitiful crew. There they stood below the mountain—the whole living world of humanity, eight people, four men and four women. After all the years and the generations and centuries only eight people, only six more than at the dawn of creation. One man and one woman then, now four men, four women to begin all over again.

Noah and his family had come down from the mountains of Ararat, where the ark had at last rested solidly, never to move again. A ship on top of a mountain.

The day had come, the bright morning, when they had chipped away the seal of pitch, and had opened the great door for all the animals to emerge from darkness and closeness and crowding into the light, into the earth with the vast sky above it—a sky full of sunshine, and no rain, and no water.

The eight people had had to stand away from the ark as in a roaring, and a screaming, and a stampeding and triumphant trumpeting, the animals had rushed forth from the ark. Galloping, leaping, plunging up against each other; dancing, galloping, thundering, they poured out of the ark in a great pent-up greed and need for the goodness of the earth.

Above the roaring and the screaming and the trumpeting and the mad, wild laughter of wild animals, over it all, there had been the rush and the flapping and the beating of wings as the birds flew out of the doorway above the stampede of animals. The animals had scattered down the mountain, the birds had winged out over the mountains, and with them on great white powerful wings had gone the swan pair. The winged swan—wing healed in the long dark ark months—flew out with his mate over the mountains in a freedom of sky and of earth and in a promise of freedom and light.

At last with their few tame animals the eight people had made the slow descent down the steepness of the mountain, led by Noah and the seven lambs grown to sure-footed sheep in the ark. The seven cows following the sheep lowed a great lowing over the mountains. The song of the cows, recast by the mountains, echoed and rolled above the eager bleat of the sheep. Noah led the way, and all the way held carefully between his thumb and finger the little olive leaf—the little shriveled olive leaf, carefully dried and preserved.

The little group of eight and their small herd reached the flatness of a fertile plain. There they camped, in a little valley under a mountain. It was a great, good day, and in distances in the mountains the freed animals called to each other in triumph as they scattered and sought new homes for themselves in the earth—the earth and its promise before them. All the earth.

But Noah, before starting anything else, built an altar on the spot where he and his sons planned a new farm at the foot of the mountain in the fertile valley. Before sowing seed, raising crops, and establishing a vineyard they built them an altar to the greatness of God and the mercy of God. Above the wet silt left by the water they built an altar of smooth, flat stones. An altar to God rose up out of the emptiness of the drowned, washed earth.

They slaughtered one of the sheep. And the smoke rose up from the altar and plumed up toward the mountains.

Suddenly the smoke did not spiral upward any more. It did not rise in a straight, thin column to the heights of the mountains, to the heights of the heavens and the greatness of God. It feathered flat over the valley.

The eight people kneeling around the altar looked fearfully at the feathering flatness of smoke over the wet land. Then they looked up to the mountains. Over the mountains rain clouds came rolling, cloud upon cloud threatening rain.

The eight in a circle about the altar cringed at the thought of still more rain. Not rain! Not rain again! Not more rain!

Suddenly above the tops of the mountains rose the sun. It rose from behind the ridge of mountains as if to peer over it to see what the only eight people in the earth were doing.

But the rain clouds rolled down into the valley, and the people bowed their heads before the coming of more rain—rain, even though the sun shone. But up in the mountains was the sunshine. And in the sunshine in the mountains was the great voice of God. The voice of God uttering a great promise to Noah and the eight and to all coming humanity, and to all life. Then, as the voice of God and the sunlight came down from the mountains, the rain clouds lifted in the mist-smoky valley, and there, arching over the valley in a majesty of heavenly colors, came a rainbow—came a rainbow in the sky.

The voice of God seemed to come to the people over the arch of the rainbow—to the frightened, kneeling eight. And the voice of God said:

"This is the rainbow,
And this is my promise—
I do set my bow in the cloud,
As an everlasting sign
That the waters shall no more become a flood
To destroy all flesh.

"While the earth remaineth
Seedtime and harvest
And cold and heat
And summer and winter,
And day and night
Shall not cease."

Then the voice of God was gone from the mountains, but the sun and the rainbow stayed. And the smoke from the altar rose again in a straight thin column, toward the mountains and into the sky, as if reaching out to the rainbow, and the everlasting promise of God. To the merciful God who had again remembered man, man in all his sin, and death and sorrow, and in all his struggle and strife. The eight people that were in the earth worshiped God, and looked at the rainbow. And the world began again.

PART III

THE BEGINNING OF A NATION

S A R A H   L A U G H E D

Now the Lord had said unto Abraham, "Get thee out of thy country, and from thy father's house, unto a land that I will show thee: And I will make of thee a great nation. . . ."

So Abraham departed. And Abraham took Sarah his wife, and Lot his brother's son, and they went forth to go into the land of Canaan; and into the land of Canaan they came. . . .

And the Lord appeared unto Abraham, and said, "Unto thy seed will I give this land."

From GENESIS 12

SARAH was in her tent. She stood in the shadows, well back of the sun-bright doorway. Abraham had three visitors, strange-looking men. Sarah had cooked for them, and now with Abraham they were eating the noonday meal under the juniper tree in the courtyard of the tents. It was the heat of the day, but Sarah stayed in the stifling tent, and now she moved next to the doorway, laid her ear against the hide wall of the tent, and listened.

She was consumed with curiosity. It was not often visitors came. And these three had not come on camel or horseback. Suddenly there they had been before the door of the tent—on foot in the heat. And Abraham, without asking them any questions, had promptly invited them to stay for the noonday meal. Now the four sat under the tree, but Sarah had not been invited to join them.

Under the tree the four men talked busily. Sarah pressed

her ear against the skin wall of the tent, strained to hear some of the talk. These certainly were strange men, and they talked strange talk. Sarah couldn't follow it. Only now and then she caught a snatch of words. . . . Then the man who sat with his back toward her suddenly raised his voice. "About this time next year Sarah will have a son."

What a thing to say! Sarah started to be offended at the way this stranger talked about her, but then for some strange reason it delighted her. And when she thought again of what the man had said, she laughed right out, laughed, and couldn't smother her giggles. She clapped her hand over her mouth. They mustn't hear her laughing, she mustn't offend a visitor; they mustn't know she'd been listening. But she couldn't help shaking with laughter—the ridiculous thing the man had said about her—the skin wall of the tent shook along with her, the tent shook with her laughter. Sarah hastily retreated to the middle of the tent.

What a story! What a tale to tell! She could imagine the camels riding, the horses running to bring the news to the tents of Canaan. Have you heard? Sarah's going to have a baby! Ninety years old, and Abraham ninety-nine, but Sarah's going to have a baby.

In the middle of the tent the old woman stood imagining it—the women of Canaan hearing the news, the women laughing, the tents of Canaan shaking with the laughter of the women.

Oh, it was so preposterously, deliciously ridiculous! Sarah pressed her hand against her mouth again to keep the giggles from escaping.

The man who sat with his back toward her—without turning, without looking back toward the tent—suddenly said to Abraham, "Why does Sarah laugh? Is anything too hard for God?"

Sarah's laughter stopped dead in her mouth. Cold dread made her shiver in the stifling tent. And in spite of herself, in her fear, she called out to the man, "Oh, but I didn't laugh."

The stranger spoke to her without turning. "Ah, but you did laugh."

And he said no more.

Sarah could say no more. She felt frightened and foolish and embarrassed all at the same time. The man had known she'd been eavesdropping. Abraham would have something to say about that after the visitors left. But it wasn't that, it was that she wanted to explain to the man that she really hadn't laughed at him. She couldn't explain, but it wasn't that kind of laughing. How could she explain that she really had been laughing at herself over something so deliciously ridiculous it couldn't possibly be believed? Not all at once—not by an old woman of ninety. She—Sarah—older than most grandmothers—to be told she was going to be a mother! Such a tale to be told in the tents!

The men had got up—they were leaving. They knew she'd been listening, and that she was still in the tent—it must be that whatever else these men still had to tell Abraham, they didn't want her to overhear. Abraham walked away with them; they talked as they walked.

From the doorway of her tent Sarah watched them out of sight, not laughing now, cold and concerned, with a chill premonition of strange things to come from the visit of these strange men, who announced strange things, who knew she had laughed, who seemed to know everything. Then Abraham and the three disappeared from sight in the heat haze over the plain.

Abraham came back alone, somber and absorbed. He must know Sarah was waiting for him, but he dropped down under the juniper tree, sat and stared. Sarah couldn't let him sit there still and staring, she had to know. She ran out to Abraham under the tree.

Abraham looked troubled. At last he told her that the three visitors had been angels of God. Bit by bit she wormed it out of him, forced him to tell her a little more. The three angels were down here to destroy Sodom and Gomorrah, the two cities of the plain. Hail, brimstone, and fire from heaven were going to rain down on the towns until there was nothing left but a smoke and a burning. God was going to destroy the two cities because of their wickedness.

Sarah listened in awe—angels of God! She had laughed at an angel of God! Oh, but surely he knew, he must know—he who knew everything—that her laughter had been a human, happy, good laughter! She in the tent imagining herself—ninety years old—a mother! She had not ridiculed, had not meant to ridicule the angel of God—not even when she hadn't known the stranger was an angel. She'd just laughed at herself, imagining herself a mother. All women would have laughed—all old women.

Sarah began to cry.

Abraham seemed to have to wrench his mind away from his own problems. "Don't worry so, Sarah. God knows there are things we humans can't accept all at once. He understands such laughter. I laughed myself when I first heard it. But I *can't* laugh about Sodom and Gomorrah. Didn't you hear? Sodom and Gomorrah are going to be destroyed!"

"Oh, no." Sarah looked aghast. "But your nephew Lot! He and his wife and daughters live in Sodom."

Abraham was solemn. "Yes," he said. "And I bargained with God for my nephew and his family."

Bargained with God? Sarah looked at her husband in cold awe. He had dared to bargain with God! And she had laughed at the words of an angel of God. What would happen to them now?

"I pleaded with God," Abraham said slowly, staring straight ahead of him, "that, if there were as many as fifty righteous people in Sodom and Gomorrah, he would spare the two towns for the sake of the fifty. . . . And God agreed."

Sarah sucked in her breath.

"Then I tugged up my courage again, and I bargained again—if there were but forty? And God agreed. I made it thirty, twenty, ten, and still God agreed. Finally, I hardly dared, but I did dare for the sake of Lot and his family, and I asked it most humbly—what if there were only five?"

"Five," Sarah said.

"And God in his mercy said that if there were as few as

five, he would spare Sodom and Gomorrah for the sake of the five."

"But your nephew Lot and his wife and two daughters—that's only four."

"I know," Abraham said slowly. "Only four. How far would you dare to go in bargaining with God?"

And Sarah said nothing.

The next day they knew that the bargain Abraham had made with God had been lost. They got up early. In the early darkness before the dawn, Abraham and Sarah stood before the door of their tent, looking out across the plain. They could not hope to see anything of the two towns, they were too far away, but they saw it in the sky. Beyond the darkness they saw a faraway flashing in the plain; they saw smoke and a bright burning among the smoke. Two columns of smoke that were two cities rose tall and enormous, and under the smoke the sky held two horrible red lights as of an awful double dawning.

Abraham uttered four awed words: "There weren't even five!"

Late in the day a rider came on a lathered horse to bring them the awful news. Sodom and Gomorrah were gone down in a brimstone lake of brine. The two cities had disappeared, in their place a lake was forming. A lake of brine in the midst of a marshy saltness was already appearing under the smoke and the stench that still overlaid the whole desolate scene. The man had been there, as near as he could get, as close as he dared.

You could see it take shape under the smoke and the smoldering—a pit of brine and brimstone, he told Abraham and Sarah. A pit? Already it was big as a lake, becoming a sea. An awful dead, still sea at the bottom of a salt marsh valley in a stench of sulphur and brimstone. You couldn't imagine the stillness where the two bright busy towns had gone down. . . .

Sarah asked it: "Did no one escape?"

"Only your nephew, Lot, and his two daughters. No one else."

Abraham asked it ahead of Sarah. "But my nephew's wife? Lot's wife? Didn't she escape?"

The man looked away, then he looked at Sarah. "That's how I came to go down to that awful place—Lot asked me to. I came on Lot and his daughters near the mountain hamlet of Zoar—they'd holed up in a cave. . . . Lot still couldn't say much, none of them could, but the way I got it from his daughters, an angel led them out of Sodom before the burning. And they were told to get on, but never to look back at the doom of Sodom and Gomorrah no matter what happened behind them. So they fled to the mountains, but after a while it seemed to them that their mother wasn't with them any more. But nobody could look back to make sure—they didn't dare. They called back, but she didn't answer. Well, finally the suspense got too awful, and they holed up in that mountain cave. In a cave they could at least turn around without the danger of seeing Sodom and Gomorrah. Their mother wasn't with them, and she didn't come. She still wasn't with them when I found them in the cave, and it was then Lot asked me would I go look for her."

The man looked away. "Well, I found her. She must have disobeyed, and turned and looked back. She'd been turned to salt! I tell you, I shuddered and got out of there. There she stood—a pillar of salt in the shape of a woman, standing there at the edge of that awfulness, staring out over the brimstone lake."

Sarah fled into her tent. She stood rigid in the middle of the tent. Lot's wife had disobeyed, and had been turned into a pillar of salt. It seemed unbelievable to Sarah—she'd known her so well. All the years Lot had been with them, she and his wife had got along so well. They'd done everything together, managing the tents and the servants, they'd done the cooking together. . . . Sarah had liked her. Oh, she'd been a bit jealous of Lot's much younger wife having two children, and she having none. Now the poor woman was a salt pillar. And now she—Sarah—was going to have a son.

Something stopped cold, dead in Sarah. She had laughed! Maybe she had laughed at the very same angel of God that had turned Lot's wife into a pillar of salt. She'd even lied to the angel—she'd said she hadn't laughed. . . .

And Sarah laughed no more in all the months.

But Sarah had a son! Ninety years old, and she had a son. And Abraham now a hundred years old, but they had a son!

This sweet day Sarah in the tent stooped over the crib where her baby lay. Her son, her baby—her son from the

Lord, even though she had laughed. She scooped up her child, she held him high in her triumph, she laughed up at him. High in her upstretched hands, the baby crowed a little laugh back at her. And at that little laugh, Sarah shouted and laughed, shouted the laughing words so that they rang from the tent: "God has made me to laugh, so that all who hear will laugh with me, for I have borne Abraham a son."

With the baby in her arms, Sarah ran out of the tent, sent the riders out, and when there were no more riders sent the herdsmen and any one of the servants who could ride horse or camel. She sent them helter-skelter in every direction to spread the news among the tents of Canaan. The tents of all the women in the land had to rejoice and laugh with her. All over Canaan the tents would shake with the joyous laughter of the women. For God had known that her laughter that day had been a woman's laughter, a good laughter. And now that she could laugh again, the tents of Canaan must laugh with her.

Let the horses and camels ride swiftly to spread the news to all the tents. "Old Sarah has a son—old great-grandmother Sarah has a baby boy."

Ah, Isaac was a good little boy. Little? Quiet, good-natured, and obedient, but not little—not any more. The way he had grown—the way the time flew—now he was already twelve years old, no little boy, no baby any more. Now her baby stood on his own sturdy legs, growing up into manhood. It was good, it was the normal course of things, but it wrenched and tugged at Sarah's heart—she would have liked to have kept him her baby forever—such a long time to wait—such a short time he'd been her baby. She had waited ninety years, and now in a few short years he was already growing away from her. Twelve years old, but Sarah still tucked him in—Isaac still slept in her tent. She had to have him near.

Sarah awoke to the sound of the splitting of wood outside her tent; somewhere in the tent area somebody seemed to be chopping wood. But it still must be dark, wasn't it long before dawn? Sarah dozed again. And then again something—the whinnying of a horse, the braying of a donkey, the beat of hoofs, some one sound or all of these—roused her. She hurried to the door of the tent, pulled back the flap. A roped donkey was staked in the yard, the donkey was braying into the distance. Sarah looked in the direction toward which the donkey brayed. Wasn't that a party of horsemen leaving the area? It was still dark, but one even looked a little like Abraham.

Sarah went back to her cot, but a foreboding rose in her like a chill. She lay listening, but all sounds were gone. One of them had looked like Abraham, the stoop of his old back, the way he sat the horse. But Abraham so old—and on a horse? On a horse, but that meant a journey. But Abraham wouldn't go on a long journey—not without telling her, that wasn't like him—not without bidding good-by to her and Isaac. Or was it something he could not tell her?

Sarah remembered that Abraham had been unusually quiet these last days. That set to his face, that stern, faraway look—he'd looked exactly that way after the angels of God had told him of the destruction of Sodom and Gomorrah. Had God spoken to him again?

Dawn came and with it the stirring of life in the compound among the tents. Sarah summoned the head servant. He was in on most of Abraham's secrets. Abraham trusted him completely. . . . Bit by bit she wormed it out of the old man. . . . Abraham had gone on a three-day journey to the top of Mount Moriah to make a sacrifice unto God there.

That made sense. That Sarah could immediately believe. It explained the chopping sounds she had heard in the night. Mount Moriah was bald at the top except for a few straggly, stunted thorn bushes—they'd have to bring their firewood if they must worship there. But why so far? Abraham was an old, old man now, why on top of a mountain?

"God came to my master Abraham," the servant said—as if that explained all.

And it was explanation enough. Whatever God had told him, Abraham would do. He would not question why he must build an altar and sacrifice on top of Moriah, when they had an altar right in the courtyard here.

Sarah dismissed the servant and went to wake Isaac. She pulled the curtains aside; Isaac was not in his bed. Isaac was gone! With a wild yell Sarah summoned the servant back again. "Where is Isaac?"

"He went with Abraham. God told my master Abraham to bring Isaac."

Then Sarah realized she had not seen Isaac in the party of horsemen because they had not taken a separate animal for the boy—he had ridden with Abraham. That was why her husband's old back had stooped so over the horse—he had bent over the child to protect him from the chill of the morning dew. But to take Isaac with him secretly—without saying a word to her, without preparing her, without even letting her kiss her son good-by . . .

It was secret and mysterious, and it was unlike Abraham. But there had been that brooding look on her husband's face—the look he always had after he'd met with God. A chill of apprehension ran though Sarah as she pondered it. And out of that foreboding an awful thought clamped around her heart. For the moment she could not breathe. She tried to think calmly, carefully, tried to remember exactly what she had seen in the predawn darkness. No, there had only been three horses, three men—Isaac she had not seen because of Abraham's stooped back. Yes, she had seen a small donkey with a bundle of kindling wood strapped to his back. She'd seen the little donkey—the night had been that clear—but then why hadn't she seen some sheep or sacrificial animal, roped and unwillingly dragging along behind one of the horses? They'd gone to sacrifice on top of bald Moriah, but they'd gone without a sacrifice? There hadn't been a sheep—Sarah was sure of it.

In all the tents round about Sarah there was the stir and noise and the chatter and clatter of the people at their breakfast. There was no one about in the courtyard. There was only the old donkey, bridled but not saddled, standing stupidly sleepy, not braying out any more, the heavy head drooping. They must have taken her foal, but had left her behind, tied in the courtyard. At once it gave Sarah a plan. If the thing

Abraham was doing was such that he wouldn't or couldn't tell her beforehand, he certainly wouldn't want her along, and he wouldn't want her to follow. She couldn't take anybody with her to guide her—they'd stop her. She had to do it alone. But the old donkey would know the way to her foal. Then the donkey must take her to her child!

Sarah untied the donkey. Awkwardly, stiffly the old woman mounted the donkey. There was no time to get a saddle or blanket—she had to catch up with Abraham and his party. To her relief the donkey was immediately willing, not mulishly stubborn. She listened to Sarah's whispers, she even trotted a little.

In the afternoon Sarah and the donkey lost the trail of the three horsemen. Sarah wandered on in the heat over the burning plain, but finally she just let the donkey do the wandering, and the donkey wisely elected to stand in the shade of a lone tree and refused to budge until evening. From under the shadowy tree Sarah sat staring into the strangeness and wildness of the hot tableland, lilting and dancing and shimmering before her. She nodded and slept in the heat, jerked awake, stared again. It became hard to separate what she saw in uneasy sleep and what she saw in her staring. She was terribly thirsty; she began to see things in the dancing, lilting heat of the day that she could not possibly see. She was in the high tableland that must eventually lead to the mountains, but in her anxiety, far out over the shimmering plains in the whiteness of heat, she seemed to see the white stillness of the dead sea. She seemed to see a white pillar rise out of the stillness in the shape of a woman. It was—it must be—Lot's wife, who had also disobeyed. Sarah sat staring in a cold sweat of anxiety. Oh, no one had expressly forbidden her to go to Mount Moriah. But Abraham hadn't wanted her to know, so he certainly hadn't wanted her there, didn't want her following. God had told him to bring Isaac—not her! Should she go back? Oh, but there was nothing. No salt pillar. No dead sea. It was only the heat and her thirst—she must be delirious. It was just the heat haze made her see things.

In the evening they set out for the mountains again, and all that night Sarah kept pressing the donkey on. She didn't know where they were, where they were going—she left it all to the donkey. They'd taken the donkey's foal, too, without explanation—poor animal. But maybe the donkey knew where her foal had gone.

All the next day—except when in the heat of the day the donkey selected a tree to stand under—Sarah wandered on at the pace of the donkey and where the donkey willed. But she took notice that the old animal was always going up to higher land, and from under the tree she sometimes thought she saw the blue haze of distant mountains. And once the donkey found a bit of stagnant water for them to drink. That night the donkey pushed on all night without any urging—seemed to be surer of where she was going, sure and eager. Once she brayed longingly.

And then, as if by sheer accident, in the night Sarah and the donkey blundered on the two servants camped with the three horses in the foothills of Mount Moriah. No, it was not by accident, the donkey must know her foal was here. As soon as Sarah dismounted, the donkey went on alone into the foothills to find her colt.

The two servants wouldn't let Sarah go on—even if she could have gone on. Sarah did not have the strength to protest. She did not argue. Even though these men were her slaves, she knew they wouldn't let her go—Abraham would have forbidden it. And she was too tired, all she could still do was to ask tired questions.

Abraham and Isaac, the men told her, had gone on on foot —Abraham carrying the pot with fire, Isaac with the wood for the sacrifice strapped to his back. With two slaves along, they'd loaded the wood on her little son to carry up a mountain! Sarah had to remind herself that Isaac was a sturdy twelve years old now, and that these were Abraham's orders. Why couldn't she ever think of Isaac in any way but as a baby?

She asked on. Slowly, warily, she came to the all-important question. "Who took the sacrifice up? What sacrificial animal did they take up with them?"

There had been no sacrifice! Now that they were reminded of it, the servants looked astounded, looked oddly at Sarah. . . . No, they were sure, their master and his son had gone up without taking anything for the sacrifice.

Could they hunt something on Moriah to use as a sacrifice?

One of the slaves looked doubtful. He was from this mountain country, he'd often hunted it, he knew Mount Moriah—

bare rock and a few thorn bushes. There was no cover for wild life there.

Suddenly Sarah jumped up, started running to where the great stern mountain loomed up in the night. The men overtook her in a few strides, and Sarah let them lead her back to the bed of skins they had laid out for her. They wanted her to sleep. Sleep! At least, rest. Well, she would rest—she had to rest, and what else could she do in the night?

Toward morning Sarah did fall asleep from sheer exhaustion. One of the young men had to shake her awake. Ah, but she was an old woman, she'd traveled far and she'd suffered much these three days—she and the donkey. Oh, but it was bright morning! Suddenly Sarah sat up. The sun was rising over Mount Moriah, the sun glistened and gleamed on the round, bald peak. The young men pointed. Then Sarah saw it, too—in the sharpness of morning sunlight she could just discern the small puppet movements of a man and a boy moving about on the bald mountain. When they moved, she could see them.

A morning haze blotted them out. When the haze lifted, burned up by the morning sun, Sarah saw only one figure moving around a square, blocklike projection that must be the altar. Where then was Isaac? Sarah turned to the young men. They with their young eyes—they mustn't fool her—was there only one figure moving about, or were there two? The men looked long, then each in turn shook his head, still looking rigidly up at the mountain, not looking at Sarah, even when they talked. Only one figure, the two men agreed, and it looked to be a man—Abraham. They couldn't see Isaac at all—but that was natural—Isaac was small.

Sarah stared up the mountain as if by riveting her gaze she could make her old eyes see what the young men couldn't or wouldn't see. She fixed her eyes on the blocklike square that must be the altar. Then she screamed it at the young men. "What then is tied down on the altar? I saw it move and struggle!"

And the young men walked away from her.

Sarah stood alone. And now as she faced the stern mountain in the pitiless light of the morning sun, she had to face the awful forebodings that she hadn't permitted herself to—couldn't have let herself—face out there in the three lonely, helpless days with the donkey. If there was no sacrifice—if Abraham had taken up no sacrifice—was then Isaac to be sacrificed? A human sacrifice? Had God demanded that of Abraham? Or had Abraham gone mad?

Then, almost mercifully, before the old woman's agonized eyes a great cloud came rolling down over Mount Moriah. The cloud covered the dome of the horrible mountain. And then, out of the cloud, over the mountain, and down from the mountain, down to the woman standing far off in the foothills, there came the great, mighty voice of God. God calling out to Abraham in the cloud on the mountain. "Abraham. Abraham." The terrible words thundered down from the mountain one by one: "Abraham, do not lay your hand upon the lad, for now I know that you fear the Lord, seeing you have not withheld your son, your only son from me."

Sarah sagged to her knees. The two men ran to her,

kneeled with her before the great voice of God, but they had to hold Sarah up. But then they looked at her in amazement —the old woman was laughing, and she could not seem to stop. Oh, at first it was hysterical, but gradually it became a serene, contented laughter. Sarah was content. For Sarah knew that if God had spoken, Abraham had obeyed his God and had not sacrificed her Isaac. She knew!

Later, when smoke rose above the stern mountain, Sarah still rested content. The smoke must be the smoke of a sacrifice, but then God had provided a sacrifice in the place of her son. She knew! Oh, God was good, and Abraham was obedient. Now at last she could rest. She ordered the young men not to wake her until they saw Abraham and Isaac coming down the mountainside.

On her bed of skins Sarah lay and went over everything in her mind. Her forebodings had been right. What she had seen in the face of her husband she had read rightly. God had tested that awesome man, and Abraham had not hesitated to offer up his only son. Sarah quailed at the thought. How could he? How could he have gone through with it, when God had promised to make of Abraham a great nation—through Isaac? Their only son, the son of their old age—when there could be no other son! But Abraham had not questioned it, he had gone through with it, until at that last hopeless, awful moment the voice of God had stopped him.

But now she had to rest and wait for Isaac. It was sure. God had spoken and Abraham would have obeyed. Now she just had to wait for her son to come back to her. It was sure, and Sarah slept.

Sarah awoke in the stillness and heat of the afternoon. Both young men were sleeping; they hadn't stood watch and they hadn't awakened her—it must mean they hadn't seen anything of Abraham and Isaac. Sarah didn't bother to waken them. Tight-lipped, she took her stand outside the canopy of hides. The desert heat bore down on her, and nothing moved. A blue haze was gathered below the mountain; it shadowed the trees and shrubs and all the dense growth of the timber line.

In the burning heat something stirred behind Sarah—then from under a thorn tree there came the old donkey with her foal, the foal nudging its mother for milk. The old donkey came trotting as if asking Sarah to protect her from her pestering young in the awful heat. The young men were sleeping.

Quietly Sarah mounted the donkey, and rode off into the foothills of Mount Moriah. The foal, nudging his mother, prodding his mother, seemed to push the old burdened donkey on toward the denseness and shade of the thick tangled brush in the cool of the shadowed mountain.

Out of the shadows and tangle—Sarah couldn't believe her watering, sun-dazed eyes—came Abraham. The donkey stopped, Sarah slid off her. But Sarah leaned so heavily on the donkey, the donkey had to stand still and let her foal drink. It was all so shadowy, such a tangle of shapes up against the mountain, but where was Isaac? It *was* Abraham. Where then was Isaac? But was it only one, or were there two? Was Abraham holding his boy by the hand tight up against him to help him get down the mountainside?

Then suddenly before her eyes, her boy, her Isaac, broke

away from Abraham, came tearing down the steep descent toward his mother. They had seen her!

Sarah ran up through the plowing deep sand toward her son. And he came plunging to her. She seized him in her arms. But in the strength of her enormous joy—grown as he was—she had to lift him, as she'd once lifted him and laughed up at him as a baby. She got him off the ground only as high as her face, but then with his surprised face right before her face, the old woman broke into a great excited laugh. But when she laughed, she had to let him down —he was too heavy. Together they laughed about it, laughed about her and her excitement—mother and son. There weren't words to express it—just deep laughter. Sarah stepped back, held Isaac at arm's length—looked at him, looked him all over. Hoarsely she asked it: "What did you offer on the altar in your place? I saw the smoke."

"A ram was caught up there by the horns in the one thorn bush," Isaac said simply. "After God spoke, and Father untied me, we offered the ram."

Sarah gathered her little son to her, and over his head she whispered it solemnly to herself. "Ah, now God has made me to laugh again, for he has given me my son again, a second time."

But she did not laugh. She clung wordlessly to her son, and together they waited for Abraham.

THE FAVORITES

And Isaac was forty years old when he took Rebekah to wife, the daughter of Bethuel the Syrian of Padan-aram, the sister of Laban the Syrian. And Isaac entreated the Lord for his wife, because she was barren; and the Lord was entreated of him, and Rebekah his wife conceived. And the children struggled together within her; and she said, "If it be so, why am I thus?"

And she went to inquire of the Lord.

And the Lord said unto her,

"Two nations, and two manner of people shall be born to thee;

And the one people shall be stronger than the other people;

And the elder shall serve the younger."

And when her days to be delivered were fulfilled, behold, there were twins. And the first was red, all over like a hairy garment; and they called his name Esau. And after that came his brother, and his hand took hold on Esau's heel; and his name was called Jacob: and Isaac was threescore years old when she bore them. And the boys grew: and Esau was a cunning hunter, a man of the field; and Jacob was a plain man, dwelling in tents.

And Isaac loved Esau, because he did eat of his venison; but Rebekah loved Jacob.

Arranged from GENESIS 25

ISAAC in his tent stared at the two boy babies on the pillow, and laughed out in amazed delight. Twenty years he had been married to Rebekah—twenty years of childlessness, and now, here, twenty years almost to the day—two sons!

All of a sudden he had two sons. Twins! Isaac poked a soft finger at the little round bellies of the two tiny mortals held out on a pillow before him by the old nurse. "But how can two brothers be so different?" he marveled. "Why, look at this one—the little red monkey—he's hair all over. But his brother—not a hair. Not even on his little head!"

The nurse, not listening, babbling herself, was pouring out to Isaac all the exciting midwife details of the birth. Isaac didn't listen to her, kept looking from one baby to the other, kept clucking and chuckling.

"The hairy one was first," the midwife told Isaac knowingly. "But if he's the firstborn, it's only by moments, for, mind you, hanging on to his hairy brother's heel came the little bald one. . . . Well, there you are—there are your two nations all on one pillow—but I've got to get back to their mother!" She covered the babies.

Isaac was startled into attention. "Two nations! What do you mean?"

"I don't know," the nurse said, turning back with the babies. "But that's what my mistress Rebekah said. She said God had told her two nations were going to be born in her tent. Well, there they are—on the pillow."

"Could I see Rebekah?"

"Not now. I'll be busy with her for quite a while. I'll call you when you may come." The nurse hurried out of the tent with the two babies.

Isaac obediently sat down. Then it amused him. This old woman now, she was his slave, he could buy her and sell her, but here were two newborn babies and she ordered him around as if he were an overgrown baby himself.

He sat chuckling over it, but as suddenly he became disturbed. Two nations! Ah, the old midwife must have got it wrong. But she'd said God had told Rebekah two nations would be born in her tent. Well, yes, but—Rebekah in the excitement and fever and agony of childbirth might have imagined and said almost anything.

It wasn't likely. God hadn't spoken to him! It was nonsense, of course—old wives' talk. If God would have spoken to anyone, it certainly would have been to him; he, Isaac, Abraham's only son. No, God had not spoken to him, but God had spoken to his father, Abraham—God had promised Abraham, that in him—Isaac—Abraham was going to become a great nation and inherit the whole land of Canaan. A great nation—not two nations! It was nonsense—old wives' talk.

Isaac sat thinking on the promises of God. They were sure, of course, but sometimes they could seem so grindingly slow. It had taken a whole century—one hundred years old his father Abraham had been, before he'd got him as a son. A great nation—and all there was of it was one lone son in a whole century. And he, Isaac, was sixty years old, and now at last two sons. One hundred and sixty years, and two tiny mortals in the middle of a pillow to become the great nation promised to Abraham. Two babies! Not much multiplication in one hundred and sixty years—and that old midwife prattled about two nations!

It suddenly struck Isaac. Why, as a nation, they, the descendants of Abraham, were no farther advanced than was all of humanity at the dawn of creation. Ages ago there had been Adam and Eve, Cain and Abel. And now as a nation here they were—still only four—he and Rebekah, Esau and Jacob. Yes, that's what he would call the twins—Esau and Jacob. . . . Name Esau for his red hair—the little hairy monkey!

Jacob and Esau. Twins. But how absolutely different! Why, his two little sons must be as unalike as Cain and Abel had been. The thought seized on Isaac, and it was so sudden and so horrible it pushed him up out of his chair. Cain and Abel—those long-ago brothers had been absolutely different, too. And Cain had killed Abel!

He stood distressed by his thoughts. He had to see Rebekah—he didn't have to obey that old slave midwife's orders—he had to ask Rebekah about the two boys becoming two nations. Rebekah must be wrong. Two brothers, twins at that, wouldn't split to become two nations. They were his sons just as much as Rebekah's, but God hadn't spoken to him—he, Abraham's son. Isaac rushed from his tent.

Twenty years went by. Isaac sat in his tent. Rebekah stood before him. She had gone to Isaac to make a complaint about Esau, but now she stood silently looking Isaac over. He'd become a sluggish, heavy old man—well, he was eighty years old. But he was too fat from eating too much, sitting too much. Always brooding in his tent! And he'd gone so completely helpless since he'd become blind. Certainly it was pitiful to be blind, but he'd given up everything—except overeating.

Aloud Rebekah said, "You'd think with all the slaves, you could call on one of them to be your eyes for you and lead you around. You never stir from this tent."

Isaac did not answer, and Rebekah knew what he felt—he'd heard all this before. There was silence again.

"Things are getting out of hand," Rebekah began once more. "But then how else could it be—you just leave everything to your two sons. You don't seem to realize how everything you inherited from your father Abraham has multiplied—everything."

Isaac shrugged. "They're young—Esau and Jacob. They're strong and healthy—and they've got their eyes."

"Eyes!" Rebekah snapped. "All your Esau has eyes for is his hunting. He just hunts and leaves everything to Jacob to manage—all the herds and flocks, all the servants, all the land—all you own. But when you die, Esau gets it all."

"Well, he's the firstborn," Isaac said stiffly.

"Yes, by moments!"

"Moments or days, he's the firstborn, and by the rights of the firstborn he gets it all—just as I got all from my father Abraham."

"But he just hunts—he'll let it go to ruin."

"Well, that's Esau's nature," Isaac said indulgently. "And

Jacob can work for him, Jacob will just have to be manager for him after I pass on."

"So Esau can hunt?"

Isaac shrugged. "You know as well as I that you're not going to change Esau. He's a hunter, a killer, and when he hunts he forgets everything else—hunger, hardship, exhaustion, all his other duties—everything! But that's what makes the real hunter." The old man talked proudly and a little wistfully.

Rebekah looked at him in disgust. Isaac had never hunted in his life, now he talked as if he were a crafty old huntsman, as if Esau took right after him. There he sat with a faint smile on his face!

"When Esau hunts," Isaac repeated softly as if to himself, "that's all he has eyes for, the game—the kill."

"Eyes!" Rebekah spat out the word. "So you think that's all Esau has eyes for. Well, let me tell you right now—your Esau's also got eyes for the heathen women of this land. Your father Abraham sent way out to Mesopotamia to fetch me as a wife for you—and I think I've been a good wife—because he did not want you to marry one of these heathen Canaanite women. But you—just so Esau hunts, just so he brings you venison. Just so you can eat. Well, then let me tell you—Esau's marrying two of these heathen Canaanites. Two!"

That shocked blind Isaac, as it had been meant to do, and for the moment Rebekah was appalled at what she had done to him. She'd just spat it out, but how it hurt him. Still . . . She flounced angrily out of the tent. Let him sit and brood on that, if he liked to brood! The thought startled Rebekah —had she meant to hurt her old blind husband that much? But he—talking so easily about Jacob working for Esau—Jacob could be Esau's manager. Just like that! Esau's slave —that's what it meant! Angry and resentful, Rebekah stormed to her own tent.

Jacob was waiting for her in her tent. He was excited. "Mother, I did it—I did it. I bought Esau's rights of the firstborn. And for nothing but a mess of stew!"

Rebekah sat down hard. "Now tell me again—slowly."

"Well, you know how Esau is when he's hunting, doesn't even think to eat, but afterward he goes wild with hunger."

"Yes, yes—I know."

"Well, I was cooking my evening meal out on the range with the herd, and along came Esau from the hunt—empty-handed for once. And when he smelled that stew cooking—I thought he was going to faint. He actually stood there swaying. And when I lifted the cover and let the steam roll up around his nose. . . ." Jacob snapped his fingers. "You know, Mother, it came to me just like that, and right then and there I told him I'd give him the whole stew if he'd give me his rights of the firstborn."

"A birthright for a stew? Everything he's going to inherit from his father?"

"Yes, I know it's hard to believe. I guess maybe he was too dazed with hunger to understand, but when he grabbed for the stew I snatched it back to make sure he'd understood. Do you know what he said?" Jacob jumped up, swaggered through the tent, began imitating Esau's gruff, throaty voice.

" 'Huh, what good's a birthright to a man dying from hunger? Give me that red stuff you've got in that kettle—you can have all my birthrights. What are you trying to do—keep on bargaining until I drop dead?' "

In spite of the amazing thing Jacob was telling her, Rebekah shook with soft laughter at Jacob's imitation of Esau. "Oh, that was good. Do it again—talk and swagger like Esau again."

Jacob grinned at her proudly, but hurried on with his story. "Mother, he actually burned his mouth wolfing down that hot stew, but down it went, and he never gave it one single thought that going down with the stew in those few moments was his whole inheritance—everything Father possesses. . . . But you know Esau—never thinking back, never thinking ahead. . . ."

"Never thinking," Rebekah said softly.

"And now it's all mine when Father dies—all mine!"

"Well, I don't know," Rebekah said thoughtfully. "Can you trade a birthright? I don't know, but maybe it's a start."

There was a call among the tents. One of the servants was going through the tent area calling out Esau's name.

"Oh, oh," Rebekah said, "I did the wrong thing! If I'd only known about you and Esau trading birthrights a few minutes earlier. I told your father the whole sickening tale of Esau's getting married to the two Canaanites. He's been brooding on it, and now he's summoning Esau to his tent. . . . You stay here, I've got to go over and listen."

Rebekah was at the tent door almost as soon as the big Esau had stomped into Isaac's tent. Esau dragged up a camp stool, settled himself beside Isaac's bed. Now his back was toward the tent opening—Rebekah could watch and listen.

"All right, my stern father," Esau was saying jokingly. "I'm settled, hands folded—the lecture can begin. What did I do now?"

"No lecture," Isaac said listlessly. "What good would it do? You do exactly as you like anyway. And I haven't the strength to cope with it any more. I'm dying, Esau—I feel it, I know it. But before I die, would you go on a last hunt for me? I'd like to have one more taste of venison before I die. Fix it the way only you can—the huntsman's way. Then when you come back I'll bless you to be sure before I die that all my inheritance from my father Abraham, and all I possess, will pass on to you as the firstborn."

For once Esau was quiet. Esau sat solemn and shaken; he was fond of his old, helpless father. At last he stooped over the bed. "It'll take a while, my father," he said quietly. "I'm just back from a hunt—three days, and I couldn't find a thing. Guess I've hunted this area to death. But no matter, I'll go up in the mountains this time, and I'll come back with the youngest, tenderest piece of venison you ever tasted —why, you'll want to live just for more venison like that." With his rough, hairy hand he pummeled his father's gray head a little bit, gave it a last little nudge. "Go on, you're not going to die." He turned, rushed blindly from the tent. Esau was crying.

When Esau had burst so unceremoniously from the tent, he'd caught Rebekah by surprise. She scurried out before him across the compound. And then he called out to her,

"I'm going right out on a hunt again, Mother. . . . Father wants some venison. Take good care of him, won't you."

Rebekah slowly turned to face him. "That'll do him good —a meal of his favorite venison," she tried to say quietly and naturally. "Good luck on the hunt, son."

He looked at her oddly. She could feel him studying her face. But her quiet words—as if she knew of nothing—seemed to convince him that she had not been eavesdropping at Isaac's tent. She looked at him steadily, tried to look cool and collected. Then to her relief Esau just waved his hand, and shouldered off to his own tent. Rebekah hurried to her tent.

She kept the flap of her tent open a slit, kept watching Esau's tent. Now at last Esau emerged, and in his hunting clothes, bow and arrows slung over his shoulder, spear in hand. He set off for the mountains. Now Rebekah turned to Jacob. "Your father thinks he's dying again—it must really have given him a shock, Esau marrying those Canaanite women. . . . I don't think he's dying at all, but this time he believes it so strongly he's sent Esau out to get him some venison and then he's going to give Esau his dying blessing as the firstborn. You'd think if he was so sure he was dying, he'd have blessed Esau first—but no matter, first or last, it means Esau gets everything we possess, and you get nothing. . . . Well, I've got other plans. But we've got to work fast, do it all before Esau gets back from the hunt. Run out and kill and dress me a young goat—save the hide, and bring that to my tent, too. I'm going now to get some of Esau's most gamy-smelling hunting clothes out of his tent. . . . Hurry, Jacob!"

"But I bought the birthright from Esau with that lentil stew," Jacob objected. "Doesn't that make me have all the rights of the firstborn?"

Rebekah shrugged. "All that means is that Esau threw his birthright away. And it's only your word against Esau's. Esau is your father's favorite, and always was; he'd take Esau's word against yours. Anyway, let's be sure, by making sure—if you get the blessing of the firstborn instead of Esau, you get the inheritance. And that will stand, that can't be withdrawn or traded." She pushed Jacob ahead of her through the doorway, and hustled off to Esau's tent.

Now mother and son were alone in the compound. Rebekah had sent the servants away. They had all been given errands and distant chores that would take them away from the tent area, and keep them away for quite a while. Rebekah and Jacob worked fast, quietly. They whispered to each other like the conspirators they were—a blind man's hearing was so keen, and Isaac mustn't hear anything suspicious.

Rebekah had Jacob cook a stew of goat's meat. "He wants it the huntsman's way," Rebekah said scornfully. "Well, you never were any kind of a hunter, but then neither was he."

Jacob kept tasting his stew, kept adding a bit of herbs, pinches of spices. In turn he and Rebekah would taste it at its various stages, trying to remember the exact taste of venison the way Esau prepared it. At last they both were satisfied—it must be as near as they could get with goat's meat. "Anyway," Rebekah whispered, "his taste isn't nearly so keen as he thinks—without eyesight half your sense of taste is gone, too. Our real problem is to make him think you're Esau."

That scared Jacob. "I don't like it," he said aloud. "Doing this to a dying man."

"He isn't dying," Rebekah whispered to make him whisper. "I know! Whenever anything upsets him, or somebody crosses him, he sits and broods and makes himself so miserable he thinks he's dying. His mother Sarah must have spoiled him to death. And since he went blind . . ."

"That's just it," Jacob whispered woefully. "It's just as awful doing it to a blind man."

Rebekah was busily cutting and shaping pieces from the hairy hide of the young goat, but she rose up, furious. "Do you think I like having to do this any better than you?" she whispered, and her whisper seemed to shout. "What do you know about love—you've only taken mine. But from the first when I came to him on the camels as his bride, he loved me, and now I'm going to destroy that love. But I'm a mother. After twenty childless years I became a mother, only to see your father love Esau, and favor only Esau from the first. Only to see Esau from the first, hairy and husky and strong—and next to him even on that first pillow you so naked and puny and weak. And as you two grew up Esau always the stronger, pummeling and punishing you even as a little boy. And always his father favoring Esau, and not punishing him, and always you running crying to me—I was your mother.

"But I was a tigress to your helplessness, and if he loved Esau, I loved you—you needed that. And I love you still, for you're still helpless over against Esau and your father. I love you so terribly that I'm going to do this awful thing, even if it destroys me."

Jacob kept backing away from her, and still she advanced on him, rushing, spitting the violent words at him, not seeing him at all, not seeing his fright and awe. Suddenly she held her breath, realizing she was too violent before this timid son of hers. She pulled Jacob to her, stroked his neck as if to quiet him, but it was to quiet herself. "God told me," she whispered softly, earnestly, quietly. "God promised me even before you were born that the elder would serve the younger —and you were the younger, if only by moments. So aren't we doing God's will?"

With trembling fingers she fitted the goatskin to Jacob's neck, forced her hands to be slow and calm and quiet. She mustn't scare the unnerved Jacob out of it now. "There," she tried to joke as she fitted the piece of goatskin precisely, "Esau's as hairy as a goat—a goat's hair ought to do the trick."

The awestruck Jacob had been rendered completely silent by her outburst. He silently dressed himself in Esau's hunting clothes, and let his mother take a tuck here and there to make the big man's clothes fit him a bit more reasonably. They were awkwardly silent now, but as she came around to view Jacob from the front, Rebekah forced a smile. "The way they smell," she whispered in his ear, "is far more important than the way they fit, and they certainly smell gamy and bloody enough."

Jacob did not answer, and his mother did not like his attempted sickly smile. She compressed her lips. "Now talk to me in Esau's voice, the way you did a while ago," she ordered to keep him occupied. "No, you don't have to whisper," she directed. "Let your father hear it, it'll make him think Esau's back from the hunt, and will prepare him when you come to his tent."

She listened, head tilted, judging Jacob's imitation of Esau, even laughing a bit to make Jacob feel more assured of himself. "A bit louder," she instructed, "he's always loud. And sound surer—he's always so sure of himself."

Once again—softly now, so that Isaac would not hear it a second time—they rehearsed the words Jacob was to speak with Esau's voice in Isaac's tent. Then they had to be satisfied—there was no more time. It all had to be done before any of the servants came back; no one must see Jacob in Esau's preposterous big hunting clothes, goatskin pasted to his hands and neck.

"It'll do," Rebekah pronounced. "Now all will depend on how you carry it off." She saw Jacob was losing his nerve again—she gave him no time. "I'm going with you. I'll have to be silent, but I'll be right there next to you in the tent." She all but shoved Jacob with his plate of goat's meat ahead of her to Isaac's tent.

Isaac was sleeping when Jacob plunged noisily into the tent. The old man awoke with a start, turned his blind eyes toward the noise. "Who is there?"

Jacob swallowed nervously. His mother gave him a sharp nudge to make him move closer to the bed. "It is I—Esau,"

Jacob gulped. Then he got hold of himself. "I'm Esau, your firstborn. I did as you told me. Now sit up, my father." He glanced at his mother, and she nodded approval—it was a good touch—that was what Esau always said—my father. "Sit up and eat this good venison while it's still hot," Jacob said loud and gruff, sure of himself now. "And after that —remember?—you were going to bless me."

Isaac dazedly sat up. "How did you find it so soon?" he mumbled. "You said it was going to take long."

At the unexpected question Jacob blurted out the first thing that must have come to his mind. "The Lord your God brought it to me," he said piously.

Rebekah shook her head at him. It was all wrong! Esau never talked piously. She was right. Isaac was at once suspicious. "Come to the bed," he ordered. "Let me feel you."

The quaking Jacob had to kneel by the bed. The old man ran puzzled hands over Jacob's hands and down his neck. "Strange, strange—the voice was Jacob's, but the hands are Esau's. Are you really Esau?"

Rebekah made frantic signals. At last Jacob understood—he pushed the plate with the so-called venison under the blind man's nose. The odors of the steamy stew distracted Isaac. He wetted his lips hungrily. "Well, yes, let's have the venison before it grows cold, and then I'll bless you."

As he ate silently, old Isaac seemed to be trying to arrange his mixed-up thoughts, but then he gave up, gave his whole attention to the good food. It was an awful wait. Jacob hardly stirred, Rebekah didn't dare breathe for fear of being

heard in the slow, munching silence. At last Isaac shoved the plate away. "Come near me again," he ordered.

Now with the spicy odors of the stew nearly gone from the tent, Isaac began sniffing Jacob's clothes. His blind hand wandered over Jacob's bowed neck and the hairy goatskin. But it was the gamy smell of Esau's hunting clothes that finally seemed to convince Isaac. His hand slowly lifted above Jacob's bowed head, and slowly Isaac pronounced the blessing that he must have rehearsed a thousand times in the old-man loneliness of his tent.

> *"My son:*
> *God give you of the dew of heaven,*
> *And the fatness of the earth.*
> *Let people serve you,*
> *Nations bow down to you.*
> *Be lord over your brothers*
> *And let your mother's sons bow down to you.*
> *Cursed be everyone that curses you,*
> *And blessed be he that blesses you."*

The solemn words ended, the old man's hands fell back on the covers. There was silence in the tent. Rebekah and Jacob, impressed and moved, did not know what next to do. Then into the stillness came a snatch of song from outside. It came from beyond the tent area, but there could be no mistaking it—it was Esau singing. It couldn't be, but it was Esau! Scared, unnerved, Jacob snatched the dish from the bed and bolted. Rebekah ran after him.

When Rebekah reached her tent, Jacob sat crowded into a

corner, cowering. The sight of his abject terror unnerved Rebekah. She fumbled the tent door shut, tried to knot the ties, stopped again to peer through a slit between two of the ties. There came Esau now, whistling and singing, a young buck slung over his shoulder. Rebekah pulled back from the slit.

Later she crawled back to the slit in the flap of the tent. And still the servants she had sent away didn't come. There was no one to help them. There was no one in the whole tent area but Esau, preparing his buck in the hot, silent compound. Behind her a sudden noise startled Rebekah. It was Jacob stirring out of his cramped corner. He seemed to have to throw himself full length on the floor in his nervous, violent fear. Rebekah ran to him. Hot and stifling as it was in the closed tent, she threw a robe over Jacob. Then she piled robe on robe. "If he comes," she whispered with her mouth close to piled robes, "I may sit right down on you, to make it look like I'm sitting on the pile of robes, but don't you stir. . . . Listen. Esau will be going to his father's tent soon now, and I'll have to creep up and listen—we've got to know what's going to develop from this—but you stay here."

With a plate of heaped venison, Esau burst into Isaac's tent. "Up, hungry old man. Up, my father," he boomed. "Look, here's young venison to bring the life into anybody ten years dead! Didn't I do well to find it so soon?"

Isaac, who had been dozing, sat up, began trembling all over. "Who are you?" he whispered hoarsely.

"Who am I? Esau, of course!"

"Who? Then who brought me venison before?" Then Isaac blurted out the helpless words. "It was Jacob, and I . . . I blessed him. Yes, and having been blessed with the blessing of the firstborn, he will be blessed, and there is nothing left."

Stupefied, the towering Esau stared down on his blind father, and a great, raw cry wrenched out of him. "Bless me, too—me too, my father."

Isaac shook all over. "Your brother stole your blessing, and with it I gave him all. All! What is there left to give you?"

Esau crumpled beside the bed and sobbed unashamedly.

Isaac sat over him, hopeless and shaken. At last his trembling hand sought Esau's head. Hardly able to lift his hand, he mumbled the few troubled words:

"Behold your dwelling shall be the fatness of the earth,
And of the dew of heaven from above.
By your sword shall you live,
And serve your brother."

"Is that all that's waiting me?" Esau croaked out. "Serve him! Serve that cheating . . . Is that all that is left for me?"

"No, not all," Isaac said, but he became terribly troubled. "I see it far away and in the latter days when you both shall have become great nations—then you shall break his yoke off your neck and be free of him."

"Thank you, my father," Esau said slowly, thoughtfully.

"I know it is your best, and your all, but if I have to wait for my descendants, wait for the centuries. . . . Well, I'm just not the waiting kind. I . . ." He did not finish the words, but suddenly whipped around, caught Rebekah standing in the doorway of the tent. She scuttled away, but it was too late.

Rebekah scurried out before Esau toward her own tent. In a few long strides he caught up with her, grabbed her savagely by the shoulder, swung her around to face him. "I knew it—you were listening at the tent earlier, when my father promised me the blessing. You had to be behind this —Jacob's only a schemer, scheming his dirty little schemes. He wouldn't have the nerve to carry it out—but you . . . Well, now listen to my last words to you, you wicked old wife of my good father. I'd kill Jacob now—I know you've got him hidden in your tent, that's where you were scuttling, weren't you?—but that would hurt my dying father. You and Jacob have hurt him enough. But remember this—the day my father dies, Jacob dies. I'll kill him."

Rebekah's mind seemed to go dead. She wrenched away from her son. Wordlessly she drew back, horrified eyes on Esau's murderous face. Her hand went to the shoulder that Esau had grabbed. She whimpered a little.

"Don't worry," Esau said. "I won't touch you again. To me from now on you are just my father's wife. I'll get at you through Jacob, when I kill your precious Jacob." He wheeled, strode away to his own tent.

Rebekah stood looking after him, fighting to get back control of herself. She still had to face Jacob. Jacob mustn't for a moment realize the extent of Esau's murderous savagery. Slowly she walked to her tent, trying to make her mind scheme and plan again. She had to see it through—finish what she had begun—see it through all the way for Jacob.

In the tent Jacob had stayed under the stifling robes. "Well, that went off much better than I'd hoped," Rebekah said cheerily toward the robes. She could make the words sound almost natural and easy, so relieved was she that under the robes Jacob could not possibly have heard Esau's murderous threat.

The robes heaved and erupted. In his relief at his mother's cheerful tones, Jacob all but burst from under the piled robes. He stood before her, anxiously searched her face for more reassurance. He streamed with sweat.

"Well," Rebekah said offhand, "I'd say it's a wonder you didn't smother under there. And I certainly can't hide you in my tent forever, so I was thinking—why don't you go visit my brother, Laban, in Mesopotamia for a few days? Esau's a little mean and bitter right now, but it looks as though he's going right out hunting again to work it out of his system. And you know Esau—one good hunt and he forgets everything. . . . But just to be on the safe side, why not visit your uncle Laban for a few days?"

Jacob nodded eagerly; for the first time looked relieved and hopeful.

"I'll go right now to fix it up with your father," Rebekah said easily. "And I think I know just how to fix it with him so he'll want you to go to Laban in Mesopotamia, too."

Rebekah came sniffling into Isaac's tent, stood sniffling before him. "I don't know," she sobbed out at last when Isaac remained silent, "I've been thinking life isn't worth living for me any more if I'm going to have two heathen daughters-in-law. Well, it's too late with Esau, but now if Jacob should also marry one of these Canaanites . . . Things were certainly better in your father Abraham's days—he sent way out to Mesopotamia to get me as a wife for you. . . . And I think I've been a good wife to you. . . ."

She waited. Isaac said nothing. The venison Esau had brought stood cold and stiff and untouched beside the bed.

"At least, I was of your own people," Rebekah said lamely into the silence.

"Yes," the blind man said listlessly, "you are right. I'll send Jacob to his uncle Laban, it's better in every way. Else what happened between Cain and Abel might well happen between these brothers. Send Jacob to me. Having blessed him, I'll now have to give him his whole stolen inheritance."

Jacob came back from his father. He was red-eyed and silent. He stood irresolute in the middle of the tent. Rebekah stepped before him. "Did he give you the whole inheritance?" she asked remorselessly.

Jacob nodded, then half turned away from her. Now that he had the whole inheritance for which they'd both schemed and plotted, he did not want to talk about it. Rebekah's lips tightened. Jacob, she knew, was already blaming her and freeing himself. "While you were with your father," she managed to say quietly, "I saw Esau leave for the mountains with his hunting gear, so now it's best you go immediately."

Jacob nodded, but it was if he couldn't pull himself away. Even as a child he'd always clung to her skirts, now, though a man, he still seemed childishly unable to make the first move of his own into the unknown strangeness. He moved to the doorway, but there he stopped again, sagging and unnerved.

Rebekah shoved the unnerved Jacob out of her tent. "Go now," she said huskily. "Don't you understand? It'll only be a few days. In a few days I'll be calling you back—you'll see, in a few days I'll be sending for you again."

She stayed in the tent, drew the tent flap shut behind Jacob. With shaky hands she knotted the ties so her son couldn't come back into her tent. She went on knotting the ties so she wouldn't see him set out like a scared, lonely child, helpless and guilty and alone—no manhood, no courage, but still her child.

Behind the tent door she kneeled and listened, but couldn't bring herself to peer through a slit to see Jacob go. Whatever she'd falsely told Jacob, she knew that he was going out of her life forever. Jacob couldn't ever come back. She'd never call Jacob back. Of one thing she was sure—if Isaac died, Jacob died. Esau would kill him.

Rebekah waited long. Now if Jacob had really gone, he must be out of sight. But had he gone? Suddenly she panicked. While she'd been plotting and carrying out her schemes, she hadn't believed for a moment that Isaac was dying. . . . But if it should be so—if Isaac died now—Esau could so easily overtake Jacob.

Almost hysterically she clawed the tent flap open. Thank God, Jacob was nowhere to be seen. He must have gone! Rebekah stole noiselessly to Isaac's tent. . . . If Isaac died now . . .

Outside Isaac's tent Rebekah stood and listened, heard nothing. She nervously sidled to the doorway. As she watched from the doorway, Isaac pulled the cold venison that Esau had left toward him, and began munching. For a moment Rebekah listened to the old man. She stood affronted, outraged—after all that had happened he could eat!

Then it struck her. She suddenly sagged where she stood, let her hands fall. Why shouldn't Isaac eat venison? He still had his venison; he still had his Esau. She was the one who had nothing left! It was she had nothing left—not Isaac.

She listened to the relentless, slow chewing in the tent. She had to clap her hand over her mouth to keep from screaming out. She forced herself to retreat slowly backward from the doorway to keep from running wildly, noisily to her tent. At last she stooped into her own empty tent.

Rebekah stood in the doorway of her own tent and stared at the rumpled, tossed pile of robes from under which the panting Jacob had heaved himself. It was as if the mute robes stared back at her.

"Wasn't I doing God's will?" she almost begged the pile of robes. "Hadn't God told me before you were born that the elder would serve the younger? And you were the younger, the weaker, the helpless one, and from the first you had no one but me. . . ."

She listened to herself, a little frightened that she was

talking out loud to the crazily upheaved robes, as if Jacob were still under them. Suddenly she rushed from the tent, fled back to her husband's tent. But when she slowed and softly drew near, Isaac was still sitting there sightlessly chewing cold venison. And Rebekah wanted to cry, but she couldn't cry. She drew back. She could weep, confess, beg forgiveness—but she knew Isaac would forgive her as easily as he sat chewing on venison, because after what she had done she did not matter to him any more. He still had Esau, still had venison—that took care of all his needs. He did not need her. Why disturb him again? Let him munch. He had that, and he had Esau, but she had lost her husband and both her sons in one day.

It was done. She had destroyed everything in one day. Maybe that is what happened to a human who meddled in the will and ways of God. Well, she had meddled, and whatever came of it now, whatever became of Jacob, she would never know. All she knew and needed to know was that in one day she had become an unneeded, unwanted old woman. An empty old woman who in destroying everything about her had destroyed herself.

Back in her tent Rebekah sagged down on the pile of robes and stared dry-eyed at the tent wall. What now would become of Jacob? She wearily drew away from the thought—there was nothing she had to do any more, nothing she could do, and nothing she could undo. It was all done. There was only the dreary knowledge—now when it was too late—that those who meddled with God's will and ways destroyed themselves.

"In a few days," she whispered drearily. "Maybe in a few days I can call him back."

She stopped it. But it began again in spite of her, because she couldn't stand the silence and emptiness in the tent. "In a few days," she began again. But she knew she could say it a thousand times, a thousand days—but it was forever. Jacob couldn't come back, she could never call Jacob back—nothing could be called back. It was done.

The empty old woman sagged on the piled-up robes and stared dry-eyed at the wall of the tent.

THE FEW AND EVIL DAYS

Now Jacob loved Joseph more than all his children, and he made him a coat of many colors. And when his brethren saw that their father loved him more than all his brethren, they hated him. . . .

And Joseph dreamed a dream, and he told it his brethren: and they hated him yet the more. And he said unto them:

"Hear, this dream which I have dreamed: for, behold, we were binding sheaves in the field, and, lo, my sheaf arose, and stood upright; and, behold, your sheaves stood round about, and made obeisance to my sheaf."

And his brethren said to him, "Shalt thou indeed reign over us, or shalt thou have dominion over us?"

And Jacob said unto Joseph, "Do not thy brethren feed the flock in Shechem? Go, I pray thee, see whether it be well with the brethren, and bring me word again."

And Joseph went after his brethren, and found them in Dothan. And when they saw him afar off, they conspired against him to slay him. And said, "Behold, this dreamer cometh. Come now, let us slay him and cast him into some pit, and we will say, 'Some evil beast hath devoured him': and we shall see what will become of his dreams."

And it came to pass that they stripped Joseph out of his coat, his coat of many colors that was on him, and cast him into a pit. . . . And they lifted up their eyes, and, behold, a company of Ishmaelites came from Gilead with their camels, going down to Egypt. And Judah said unto his brethren, "What profit is it if we slay our brother. . . ? Come and let us sell him to the Ishmaelites."

And they drew and lifted up Joseph out of the pit, and sold Joseph to the Ishmaelites for twenty pieces of silver. . . .

And they took Joseph's coat, and killed a kid of the goats, and dipped the coat in the blood; and they brought it to their father, and said, "This have we found: know now whether it be thy son's coat or no."

And he knew it, and said, "It is my son's coat: an evil beast hath devoured him. . . ."

And all his sons and all his daughters rose up to comfort him; but he refused to be comforted.

From GENESIS 37

THE haunted old man sat in the open doorway of his tent. Old Jacob sat in the small square of shade cast by the little canopy over the doorway, and stared rigidly out at the burning land. His hands lay heavy in his lap.

Dust whirled above the land as far as eye could see. In the sky the sun was a flat, gray disk, trying to drill through the dust rising up from the land. The land was going up to the sun in dust. It swirled up to the sun in impenetrable miles of dust.

Jacob looked at it with hurt eyes. He loved this land. Other beings you loved with the heart, but land—land you lived on, walked over, worked over, scarred with your plow—you loved with your lifeblood, every day and year of the life you had given to it.

As if he could stand the frightfulness no longer, Jacob turned away toward the open doorway of his tent. There was no one in the tent. Only a dust-covered coat hung against the one wall. Jacob stared at the empty coat—Joseph's coat.

There it still hung, and there it had hung since Joseph died.

Thirteen years ago he had sent Joseph out to Shechem where the ten sons of Lea, Joseph's half brothers, were herding the flocks. A wild beast had destroyed Joseph, and only Joseph's many-colored coat, bloodstained and torn, had come back. There it hung.

The old man turned restlessly from the coat back to the dying land. As if to make it pitilessly clear to Jacob that his beloved land was dying, the sun that moment drove in between great dust clouds and stood clear and coppery over the ranges and hills. With dust-reddened eyes the old man stubbornly looked at his land. Skeletons of cows bleached against all the hills. Among the skeletons lay dead cows, bloated and unburied and indecent—they died too fast to bury them all. Three sheep and a few faraway goats wobbled along the ridge of a sand dune that had once been rich grazing land. Jacob's hands fell back in his lap. Ah, it was done, it had died, this land of Canaan, the land he loved.

Then the sudden, startling thought struck Jacob and he half whirled to the coat hanging behind him in the tent. He muttered it aloud. "What Jacob loves—dies!"

Wasn't it so? He had loved his mother Rebekah. But his mother had sent him away, almost pushed him out of her tent and sent him to her brother Laban, for fear Esau would murder his brother Jacob. But Rebekah had died long before Jacob could return to Canaan. He had never seen his mother again.

He had loved Rachel, his second wife—loved her as his own soul. All those years in Mesopotamia—twenty years—

serving his uncle Laban, he had dreamed of returning to Canaan with Rachel. He had pictured beautiful Canaan to her. He had pictured to himself showing the beloved Rachel his beloved land. Rachel had died as they'd come into Canaan.

Rachel had died in giving birth to his youngest son, Benjamin. After Rachel's death, he'd had Benjamin, and he'd still had Joseph, Rachel's oldest son. Ah, he'd had Joseph and Benjamin, sons of his beloved Rachel. Oh, he had ten other sons by his other wife, Lea, but his love for Rachel had fixed itself only on Joseph. And he had loved Joseph as his own soul. Thirteen years ago Joseph had died.

Then there had been nothing left to love but the land and little Benjamin. But he had almost not dared to love Benjamin. Evidently he must have believed it all along—all these thirteen years—that what he loved died. But he had never admitted it to himself until a moment ago when he had blurted it out to himself. "What Jacob loves—dies."

No, he hadn't dared to love Benjamin, the little brother of the beloved Joseph. He had not dared to admit his love for Benjamin even to himself. But there it was—he loved Benjamin as his own soul.

Now the land was dead and dying. "Even land dies because I love it," the old man said bitterly. In saying it out loud, he was somehow startled. But why hide it from himself any longer? The evil he had done to his father Isaac and his brother Esau in cheating and robbing them of this precious, beautiful land had followed him all the days of his life. God moved grindingly slow, but slowly, one by one, He had taken away all that Jacob loved. And now the land. He—Jacob—

had done evil to his own flesh and blood, now evil pursued him to its evil end. And now he was a helpless old man—now there was nothing he could do but wait out his few and evil days on the dying land. It wouldn't be long—when land died everything died. Benjamin, too!

The thought shook Jacob. Benjamin would die, too! If the land died, Benjamin would die. And there was nothing to do. Evil was following him to its bitter, inexorable end. All his life scheming and plotting and planning had been his second nature, but he had never given thought that land could die—not the rich land of Canaan. Now there was nothing to plan, nothing to do. No—no more planning, no more scheming. Just let the hands fall, let the land die, and Benjamin, too. Just wait out the few and evil days still left to him. What could man do over against God?

The street of tents of the compound continued to lie silent and dead, every tent shut tight against the blowing sand and dust. Only Jacob's tent was open, and Jacob kept stubbornly to the open doorway of his tent—as if to punish himself, as if he must see the land go dusty swirl by dusty swirl to its sure death.

Now beyond the stillness of the double row of tents of the compound there was a sudden running and pounding and yelling. Jacob stood up. Oh, it was only Benjamin trying to rope a young calf—the stillness and the dullness must have been too much for the boy. He and the calf came tearing down the street of tents in a storm of stirred dust. Benjamin shouldn't be chasing the starved little animal.

Jacob started to call out to Benjamin, but he sat down again. He hadn't the heart. Let the boy have his fun; he alone must still be able to find fun in this frightfulness. He was young, he didn't see death coming to all of them.

Strange, Jacob mused, he hadn't loved Benjamin as a little child. After the death of Joseph his heart had fixed on Benjamin, but he hadn't dared to love Benjamin. He had been terribly careful with this his last love. He'd tried to love Benjamin intelligently. He'd never treated Benjamin with that complete indulgence with which he had thoroughly spoiled Joseph. He'd tried not to set him apart from his half brothers, the ten sons of Lea. He'd never given Benjamin special gifts, special clothes, and certainly never a many-colored coat—the old coat of Joseph hung in the tent forever to prevent him from doing that.

But what it amounted to was pure superstition. What it amounted to was that all the time he had tried to hide his love for Benjamin from God. He had fought with himself to keep from wrapping Benjamin in his fatal love, since what Jacob loved God killed. As if God didn't know the heart. You couldn't help love—you couldn't hide it. But strange how lighthearted and new and young he felt now that he'd accepted the will of God, and now that he'd spoken out his hidden love for Benjamin—if only to the coat in his tent.

Ah, but there was Benjamin again—roping another bawling calf. He shouldn't! The poor animals were far too starved.

Once more Jacob stood up. "Bennie," he called out. "Benjamin," he sternly corrected himself. "You come here."

But Benjamin was far too absorbed in the exciting struggle

with the calf to listen or hear. Now, finished with roping the calf, Benjamin came at last. Panting with excitement, he stood before his father. Jacob remembered to be stern and cool. "You know better than that—you shouldn't maul those poor starved calves."

The boy's excitement fell dead. "What is there to do?" he said resentfully. "Everybody just sits around in the tents."

Jacob was at once sorry, at the same time knowing he had nothing to be sorry for. Ah, it was hard not to be indulgent. Maybe when you got old you got like a child yourself. He actually felt wretched that he had suddenly shut off the boy's fun. . . . Ah, it was good for an old man to have a child in his old age, but he mustn't be childish himself. He smiled a slow smile at his disapproving son. "What is there to do? I'll tell you something to do—instead of calves will you round up your ten brothers for me and tell them to come to my tent? Only—don't do it with ropes!"

Benjamin whooped with laughter, went away, laughing.

Proud of himself and his little joke, the old man started to sit down, but his eyes went to the coat in the tent, and he smiled a little. The small pride in his little joke seemed to have changed things. Somehow he was inordinately proud that he, an old man, could still make a joke that could make his young son yelp with delight. He hadn't intended to do anything more—give Benjamin an errand to do, and make him laugh; but now, having done it, he somehow could no longer sit hands in lap and let everything go to dust and death. He once more looked at the coat. No, it didn't matter for him; old as he was, he was more than willing to die with his land, but he wouldn't be Jacob if he didn't plan and scheme and maneuver until the end—if not for himself, then for Benjamin and his other sons and their families. It all seemed to wait for him.

The ten brothers came, and then even Benjamin. Coiled rope in hand, he stood in the midst of the men. The older ten had unconsciously formed their usual half circle as they came to stand before their father. They were solemn and somber, with little to say. Jacob studied their faces but asked no questions. They got out on the ranges and among what was left of the herds and flocks—they saw even more than he. "I called you," Jacob said, "because I've been hearing things these last days. You know how wayfaring strangers come by, and, seeing me sit in the door of my tent, they stop for some talk in the shade and a drink of water. That way you hear all kinds of things, but three times these last days I've been told that there's grain to be bought in Egypt."

"The famine's in Egypt, too," one of his sons said. "It's over the whole earth."

"I know. But these wayfarers tell me there's a man in Egypt—he's been placed just under Pharaoh—who foresaw the coming of this famine seven years before it came. In the good years he gathered up the grain of Egypt, and stored it. Now in this famine he's selling that stored grain back to the people—the Egyptians are even selling him their land, just to get food. Bit by bit he's buying up almost all Egypt for Pharaoh. . . . But what's important to us—they tell me he'll also sell grain to people from the countries round about."

He looked at the ten men for some comment, but they all stood waiting. Old as he was, these grown sons with families and children of their own—even grandchildren—still depended on him to make all the plans and decisions. It oddly pleased old Jacob, but he spread his hands palms upward in a helpless, modest gesture. "Well, you know rumors. It's a long hard journey to take on a rumor—have we got ten horses left? If I send all ten of you on horseback, you can carry more grain, and you can get back fast. It has to be fast, we've no grain left."

Benjamin stepped out of the group. "Why'd you leave me out?" His young face was ugly. "Why can't I go, too? I've got a horse!"

Jacob's heart turned. He cast about in his mind, unsure again. Why couldn't the boy go? It would be an adventure for him, get him out of this wretchedness. But as he considered it, Jacob knew he need not consider it; he couldn't let Benjamin go. Send him away, perhaps to his death, as he had once sent Joseph to his awful death? The old haunting thought took hold of his mind—if what he loved died, Benjamin couldn't escape, God would find him at home or in Egypt. . . . He gazed somberly at Benjamin, ignored the boy's dark look.

"If all ten of you go," he said heavily, "pick the ten best horses we have left, and get back fast. It's Egypt or starve, and I only hope and pray there is such a man in Egypt—he must be a wizard—who had the foresight to store up grain for these awful years. Well, what do you think?"

"We'll try anything," Simeon began to say for all of them,

but Benjamin stepped right before Jacob, fixed his father with his sullen look.

"No, Bennie, you stay here. The rest of you get ready and get going. As it is, we'll just have to eat what's left of the dying cattle, and all that's left of them is bone and sinews." He looked at Benjamin. "Maybe it's a good thing—they'll chew longer, and that ought to help make them last until your brothers can get back," he tried to joke.

Benjamin angrily turned, stamped way from him—big boy steps. "Always treating me like a baby!" he said in a mutter his father was meant to hear.

The old man sat alone again.

His ten sons were gone too long. By Jacob's best and most generous reckoning they ought to have been back from Egypt more than three days ago. What was keeping them? Day after day Jacob sat in the doorway of the tent, his old eyes peering out to the hot horizon where the dust devils danced. Every day he kept Benjamin going to the top of the first hill to look with his young eyes for any sign of the ten horsemen. Only to the top of the first hill—Joseph's hill. As he worried and fretted about his ten other sons, Jacob could not bear to have Benjamin go beyond his sight.

But now—where was Benjamin?—wasn't that a dust storm in the distance among the low hills? But today the land and dust lay still—there was no wind. This must be a storm of dust kicked up by horses. "Bennie," he yelled hoarsely. "Benjamin . . ."

His old eyes had not deceived him. Benjamin came running

to him—he too had seen the horses coming. "Are they loaded? Are the horses loaded, Bennie?"

"It looks to me like they're sitting between loaded bags," Benjamin guessed hopefully.

Taking his youngest son tightly by the hand, old Jacob went slowly out across the starved fields toward Joseph's hill. They got but a little way, then the horses stormed over the top of the hill and surrounded them. Joyful and relieved, old Jacob stood amongst his sons and the horses. They had grain—bags of grain—but they were completely worn out and exhausted. The ten men dismounted, stood around Jacob heavy and worn.

Yes, it had been a hard trip—hard and long. Yes, they'd got all the grain they could carry, and at not too gouging prices. . . . And what did Jacob think? They'd even met the vice-regent of Egypt—that wizard, just under Pharaoh, who'd predicted the coming of the famine and had stored up the grain. In fact, the great vice-regent was the one who had sold them the grain. . . .

Oh, he certainly was a wizard—he knew everything. Strange, though, a smart man like that—he was also mean and petty. Sort of a childish tyrant.

Jacob stood joyfully confused among the talk, twisting and turning his gray head in trying to keep his best ear to all the talk.

"Where's Simeon?" Benjamin beside him said shrilly.

"If just one of you would tell it—slowly and in order," Jacob said plaintively.

"Well, then, let me tell it," Judah said loudly to all his

brothers. He came to stand right before Jacob. "Father," he began carefully, "you guessed right when you thought that man must be a wizard—he knew everything, everything! He even knew all about us. Mind you—we didn't ask to be taken before him—we'd have bought grain from anybody, but the border guard took us right to this great vice-regent of Egypt. But, Father, listen—we were taken before him as spies! As spies! We ten simple shepherds! But that's what that vice-regent said we were—spies."

Jacob stiffened, the blood drained from his face. His eyes ran uneasily from son to son, his lips moved as if counting.

"Where's Simeon?"

"We told him," Judah said slowly, "that we weren't spies, just shepherds, ten of twelve brothers who'd come from Canaan to buy grain. We kept telling him that that's all we were—just shepherds who lived in Canaan with our father and a younger brother."

Judah waited a moment to let that sink in. "Father, when we told him that, he struck like a snake. We had said we were twelve brothers; that wasn't twelve, that was only eleven. We explained that we'd meant that we'd been twelve, but that one brother had died some years ago. After that he didn't believe anything we said. He just kept saying, 'You're spies. You're spies.'

"And he put us in jail—all ten of us. Well, after three days he finally let nine of us go, but he's holding Simeon—as a hostage. Put him in chains right before our eyes!"

Jacob's stunned, toothless old mouth fell open, his fearful eyes fixed on Judah, and wordlessly his eyes seemed to beg

Judah to tell him all. His lips began to move. "Judah, just stop preparing me—tell me all. Just tell me all."

"Listen, Father," Judah said uneasily, "that man in Egypt still believes we're spies. . . ." Then Judah got it over in a rush. "He's holding Simeon, but he's holding him only until we bring Benjamin to prove we were telling him the truth. And if we don't—Simeon gets sold as a slave, or worse."

The old man shook. His trembling hands had to catch hold of Benjamin's shoulders so he could steady himself. His face worked, then he found words. "Fools!" his voice croaked at them over Benjamin's shoulder. "You fools! Why did you have to tell that man about Benjamin? Of all the things you could have told him! Why that? I lost Joseph because of you, so now you're going to rob me of Benjamin. I knew you hated Joseph, and you must hate Benjamin, too."

Judah shrugged helplessly; his eight brothers stood sullen and outraged. And Benjamin, held by his father's fierce grasp, looked down at the ground in shame and confusion. Now Reuben, Jacob's oldest son, stepped up. He resentfully shoved Judah aside; his mouth was hard and cruel. "Judah tried to break it to you carefully, but it seems you don't want it that way—then take it this way from me. Judah hasn't told you all, he was sparing you. I'm not sparing you—why should I? We're all grown men but you treat us like witless five-year-olds before young Benjamin. What Judah didn't tell you is that when we got back to the border of Egypt, we found all the money that we'd paid to the vice-regent for our grain back in the mouths of the sacks, and we didn't dare go back with the money—not even with Simeon held prisoner there. But when these sacks of grain are gone, we'll have to go back or starve." Reuben paused, squared his shoulders. Then he counted out the hard, slow words to his old father. "Well, we're fools, as you said. But you're always so proud of your clever scheming and planning, so you figure what to do. Since we're all fools—you start scheming now."

Jacob's lips moved, but he uttered no sound. For the first time in his life he felt completely outwitted. The faraway tyrant in Egypt, having grain, having Simeon in prison, had the complete upper hand. There was no way to turn. It was go back or starve. They were at the Egyptian's mercy—if that man had mercy. Jacob let go of Benjamin's shoulders, turned away from his sons, and limped back to his tent alone.

The grain the nine brothers had brought back from Egypt was gone. They should have returned to Egypt days ago, but there was no reasoning with Jacob. In his way Jacob was as childishly unreasonable as that petty vice-regent of Egypt. Jacob simply would not hear of Benjamin's going along with his nine brothers to Egypt. He didn't even seem to consider it, though it meant sacrificing Simeon to slavery or death! There he sat stubborn and mute in the doorway of his tent. He wouldn't listen to any of them.

This day it was Judah's turn to try it again—reason with their father. Judah was desperate. He did not spare Jacob. "Father, now I'm going to spell it out for you as to a little child. It has come to this—if you don't let Benjamin go, we don't go. We'll simply all starve here—your Benjamin, too. We know how you feel about us, Lea's sons—you seem quite willing to sacrifice Simeon to Benjamin. So you love Benjamin! But Simeon is a father, too. Simeon loves his children, too. And Simeon's little children love and need him more than Benjamin needs you. But away with them, away with Simeon, away with all of us, if only you can save your precious Benjamin!"

Old Jacob stared away across the land.

The wretched Judah stepped close, screamed it in Jacob's ear. "Don't you realize yet that you've nothing to decide? That it isn't in your hands—isn't in ours? If we don't go back with Benjamin, we starve—all of us. Listen, I have two children, I love them, but if I don't bring Benjamin back to you safe and sound from Egypt, you may kill my children." The man, having slammed out his desperate offer, stood wearily still.

Jacob tossed it aside as if it were nothing. "Why did you have to tell that Egyptian tyrant about Benjamin?" he said pettishly.

"Father, didn't you hear? I'm vouching for Benjamin! No harm shall come to him. And if that Egyptian should get so low as to want to keep Benjamin, I'll take Benjamin's place—I'll somehow persuade that man, so your son can come back to you."

Old Jacob looked directly at Judah, and a slow tear rolled unheeded down his face. Poor Judah, the poor man—ah, the hopelessness and power of hunger—didn't he realize these were powerless promises; and offering him his children—their grandfather might kill them! He stared out across the land. His mind was made up. It was only that it was almost impossible for him to give utterance to the words of permission. Judah had unknowingly spoken it—it wasn't in his hands, it was in God's hands, and God moved in his own way. He, Jacob, had not let Benjamin go on the first trip to Egypt, thinking in that way he could keep Benjamin from the evil that hung over all those he loved. And now look, a complete stranger in faraway Egypt had made it so that he could not keep Benjamin after all. He had lost to a stranger. But it wasn't the stranger, it was God. God's way, God's means, God's will.

Softly he said the words to Judah. "Take Benjamin, take presents for the Egyptian despot, and plenty of money. Take back the money you found tied in your grain sacks. And if then I must be bereaved of all that I love, then I must be bereaved. It is God's will." The old man wept a little. "Go, Judah, but go fast. Come back as soon as you possibly can. Come back to me, try to come back—all of you. Now go."

And Judah turned and ran like a colt to the tent area.

As if all his sons had waited for this decision, they went. They'd all been ready, they had Benjamin ready. They'd have gone this day, Jacob suspected, with or without his permission—taking Benjamin. He was somehow glad they had waited for his word, proud now that he had given his word. And in his small pride he turned to the dusty coat in the tent. "Ah, they're all good sons in my old age. But I, it seems I can only bring them evil."

There they came now on their horses, the nine brothers with Benjamin in their midst. There they went now toward the first hill, Joseph's hill, and Benjamin waved wildly—ah, it must be high adventure to the boy, much better than roping wobbly calves. From Joseph's hill Benjamin seemed to be yelling something at Jacob as he wildly waved good-by.

Suddenly Jacob jumped up so hard he knocked over his camp stool, but he scrambled stiffly over the tumbled stool, and all but dived into his tent. He jerked the tent flap shut, he fumbled with the ties, then just held the flap shut with both clenched hands.

Please God, let Bennie not shout the words of Joseph from Joseph's hill. He mustn't yell, "In a few days I'll be back. . . . You'll see . . . in a few days." The words of Rebekah, the last words of Joseph.

Oh, it was superstitious, it was childish, he knew, but the old man kneeled at the tent door holding it shut with both hands, and his rigid back was turned toward the empty coat.

They were gone. All sound of the horses was gone. Fearfully Jacob came out of the tent, made a labor of righting the camp stool before he stared out over the land. They were gone. The old man stared across the empty land unseeing, and sat down. The days of his old, helpless waiting in the doorway of his tent had begun.

In Egypt the ten brothers were halted as they crossed the border. They were searched—even Benjamin. Then the mounted, armed guards rode ahead, beside, and behind them, and once more took them to the house of the vice-regent of Egypt.

It looked like nothing but more trouble again. But it was

hard to guess what kind of game the strange Egyptian was planning to play with them this time. They were led into the great dining room of the vice-regent's house. Alone at the huge table sat their brother, Simeon, released from prison and decked out in new Egyptian clothes. The brothers were given no chance to question Simeon. The vice-regent came into the room, and behind him the interpreter. Now he was formal. Through the interpreter he formally asked them to sit down at the banquet table. Asked them! He told them exactly where to sit, and in the exact right order of their ages, from Reuben down to young Benjamin. . . . Well, maybe he'd questioned Simeon.

Then it became almost funny—if everything hadn't been so tense and desperate, it would have been funny, except that you didn't laugh with a great vice-regent present. The slaves came in to serve them. But they served Benjamin first! And they heaped food and food on Benjamin's plate—food enough almost for all of them. But who could tell what childish nonsense this vice-regent of all Egypt would think of at any moment?

Now the vice-regent sat down, but he sat down at a separate table. Then he had the interpreter carefully explain that Egyptians didn't sit at the same table with Hebrews—Hebrews were an abomination to the Egyptians. Nothing was funny any more.

The vice-regent at his table raised a big silver goblet as if to propose a toast. Instead, he asked through the interpreter, "Is your father well?"

All eleven brothers bowed their heads to him and in their

eagerness to please almost intoned together, "He is well, my lord."

The vice-regent looked hard at Benjamin. "Is this the youngest brother about whom you told me?"

They inclined their heads. "It is, indeed, my lord."

But when they lifted their heads the vice-regent was rushing from the room. After a little interval he came back into the room, but he almost looked as if he'd run out to cry, quickly wiped his face, and come back again. He must be insane!

Now that he was back at his table and somewhat composed, the great man solemnly raised his silver goblet again, and solemnly intoned a toast—but to Benjamin. He toasted a boy! They all inclined their heads again as the interpreter intoned in Hebrew, "God be gracious to you, my son."

Benjamin looked red and confused, and didn't know what to do or say. The great man did not seem to notice. The banquet began—if it was a banquet and not a last gallows meal.

At last the banquet was over. Hungry and starved as they'd come, it had been wasted on them. It had turned out about right—did that Egyptian know everything?—Benjamin had been the only one that could eat. And between wolfing his heap of food Benjamin had kept gaping around the great room, at the hangings and the lamps and chandeliers. Half the time they'd had to kick him under the table—he kept staring at the great vice-regent. Ah, but now it was over, and under the circumstances everything had gone wonderfully well—perhaps too well. But as mean and suspicious as he'd been the first time, so gay and lighthearted the Egyptian was now. Who could puzzle him out?

The eleven brothers set out at daybreak. The house of the vice-regent was still asleep. The brothers quietly loaded the horses with the grain that had been provided them the night before, and stole away in the dawn. The horses were so loaded they'd have to go slow, but if only they could make it across the border before the vice-regent awoke—before that strange man could think up other fantastic schemes or mean tricks. This time Simeon was with them—Benjamin, too, thank God. Now if only they could make it to the border. . . .

They were stopped at the border. One of them, the enraged captain of the guard told the brothers, had stolen the silver goblet of the great vice-regent. The precious, magic goblet, the sacred divining cup by which he foretold the future. The very cup by which he had foretold the famine and saved all Egypt. The sacred silver cup—of all things to steal!

It was so preposterous, the brothers laughed about it, even though it was a hollow laugh. They let Simeon take over for them—Simeon had learned a few Egyptian words in the Egyptian prison. "Tell them we're innocent, Simeon."

"We steal?" Simeon spluttered. He managed a false little laugh. When Simeon laughed the others all took their cue from him and showed their teeth in tight, artificial grins. Now Simeon was trying to chuckle. They showed their teeth again.

"Why—of all things—would we take the silver cup?" Simeon hackled in part Egyptian, part Hebrew. "No, what we need is food for our starving families—we're starving, we'd hardly think of a silver cup. . . . Hah, if you find that cup on one of us—well, as far as we're concerned, you can kill him.

"Can't he?" Simeon appealed to his brothers. And they all hurriedly nodded and set their teeth in uneasy grins.

The sacred silver divining cup of the great vice-regent of Egypt was in Benjamin's sack of grain.

There was nothing more to be stammered or said, nothing more to be grinned. Somehow they fumbled the ties around their sacks, struggled the sacks back on their horses. The guards did not lift a finger now. In awful silence they were led back to the vice-regent's house. In single file, guards marching tightly beside them, the eleven brothers were led before the vice-regent of Egypt. They threw themselves on the floor before his feet. Judah managed to stammer out, "We're all your slaves. We'll all be your slaves forever."

But the vice-regent was stern and cool. Through the interpreter he said quietly, "That's noble of you, I'm sure, but all I want is the one who stole the silver cup. The rest of you can go in peace to your father."

From the floor Judah lifted his face and stared up at the man in agony. Then he jumped up. Guards grabbed him, but he tugged them along until he stood right before the vice-regent. "Take me," he screamed in Hebrew to the man. "Take me! I vouched for the boy. I promised our old father I'd bring Benjamin back. Our father will die of sorrow if the boy doesn't come back to him. He can't go through it again. Benjamin's brother, Joseph, was torn to pieces by a wild animal, and we had to bring our father that news. Now if we come

without Benjamin . . . Take me! I'll be your slave. . . . Kill me. Anything! I . . ."

Judah's mouth fell open. Before him the vice-regent of all Egypt stood crying like a child. "I'm Joseph," the Egyptian wept. "Joseph! Don't you understand? I'm your brother Joseph!"

Judah's lamed hands fell to his sides. Behind him his brothers lifted their terror-stricken faces to Joseph, then in their terror actually tried to push themselves backward over the floor.

But Joseph stood quietly. "Don't be afraid. No harm will come to you. I know that thirteen years ago you meant to kill me, then sold me into slavery instead. But what you meant for evil God must have meant for all our good. This famine has still five years to run. But there's plenty of food in Egypt, and good grazing land in the province of Goshen. . . . So go back now. Hurry back to my father. Then come back with our father and all your wives and children, and all you own, and take everything to the land of Goshen. I've got permission from Pharaoh. I've got everything prepared and ready. . . . Yes, take my father to Goshen—I'm sending a chariot with you in which to take him there, and I'll come and meet him in Goshen. Go now—I can't hold out much longer, I can't wait. Young fresh horses and the chariot are waiting for you outside. . . . Go now, and I'll meet my father in Goshen."

Jacob was sitting in the doorway of his tent in the helpless long wait of the old. But wasn't that a cloud of dust? Not dust devils—dust raised by storming horses! Ah, yes—now there they came storming down over Joseph's hill. But why did they run their loaded horses and come sweeping down on him and his tent as if they were going to ride it down? Now two separated from the clustered thundering horses. It was Benjamin! And right on behind Benjamin—why, it was Simeon! Now Benjamin whipped his horse, stormed on ahead, yelling and waving at him, and yelling again. "It was Joseph," Benjamin yelled to him over the neck of the horse. "The great man in Egypt is Joseph!"

Jacob heard the words, but did not try to understand them. He sat rigid and still, waited. Suddenly Benjamin drew in his horse, and also waited—no, his brothers were calling him back. Now they all came on, drew up, dismounted, and came walking to him. Unconsciously they formed their half circle before him as they'd always done. But Benjamin, suddenly looking scared, withdrew behind the half circle, half hid behind big Judah.

Jacob's sons began to tell Jacob, and their halting slow words said what Benjamin had yelled—Joseph was alive. . . . No, Joseph had not been torn to pieces by a wild animal! They hackled it out, each one took his turn. Yes, that was blood on Joseph's coat hanging behind Jacob in the tent, but it was the blood of a goat. They'd butchered a young goat to make it seem it was Joseph's blood.

Confused, Jacob turned toward the coat, confusedly turned back to the half circle. The ten men, his sons, stood before him like guilty little boys, but still Jacob's mind wouldn't close itself around the thing they were telling him—the horrible deed of thirteen years ago that his sons only now were confessing. The old man looked from the one to the other—thirteen years they'd let him sorrow and suffer. . . . Where was Benjamin?

No, they hadn't killed Joseph. Each of the men in the half circle solemnly repeated it to make Jacob understand. Oh, they'd intended to kill him, but a caravan of Ishmaelites had come along, and they'd sold Joseph to them, and the Ishmaelites in turn had sold Joseph in Egypt. Yes, Joseph had been a slave, but now he was the vice-regent of Egypt. It had all ended so well. It was just as Joseph had said to them: "You meant it for evil, but God meant it for good."

Again somebody slowly repeated Joseph's words to Jacob, carefully, slowly—God had meant it for all their good—to impress their father, have it help soften the enormity of their crime of thirteen years ago. Now they just stood and waited for him. . . . Where was Benjamin?

Oh, there he was—half hidden behind Judah. Jacob closed his eyes. He began to shake violently. Two of his sons rushed up to brace him, keep him from falling off his backless stool. But with closed eyes Jacob was seeing that other shaking of his own father, when he had so cruelly deceived old, blind Isaac. Now he—Jacob—had been treated ten times more viciously by his own sons. . . . Oh, Joseph had said it so right—they had meant it for evil, but God had turned it to his own good. He, too, when he had deceived his blind father and cheated Esau, had meant only evil, and the evil had followed him all the years of his life. . . . But now this—what his sons had done to him—was a cruelty ten times greater! Ten times? Had he shown blind Isaac any mercy? Then wasn't what his ten sons had done to him no more—maybe exactly what he had deserved? And if so, then what could he now say to his sons? Accuse—reproach them—he? Flail them with bitter words? What was there for him to say? It was only for him to forgive. . . .

Jacob opened his eyes, looked at his sons standing there almost as if they had heels dug in for the lashing of his tongue. "It is enough—it is goodness enough," he said in a clear, firm voice. "Joseph is alive. I am going to see him before I die. It is enough. . . . And I—I an evil old man—if I have anything to forgive, I forgive you, my sons, for now I have seen it as Joseph saw it—what I, what you meant for evil, God meant for good."

As he said it, suddenly the haunted, guilty old man had peace. Knew peace. Now at the last in forgiving his sons—as Joseph had forgiven them—it was as if he could forgive himself. Forgive himself as God had forgiven him—God who was good, and even turned evil to good at the last. "Now I've got to go to Joseph," Jacob said to his sons, and it was a plea.

Benjamin crowded between Judah and Reuben. "But, Father, that's just exactly what Joseph wants, too! That's what Joseph said. He's got everything ready, he's got a whole province for us—Goshen, that's its name. . . . But wait till you see. . . ." Benjamin was suddenly too excited to tell it. He tore away from the group, ran like a colt up Joseph's hill.

The brothers explained to the old man what Joseph had told them—they were all to come to Goshen in the five terrible years of famine that still were coming. They talked of the long preparations that must be made for the great journey. It would be a slow, long journey with their families and all their possessions.

Jacob stood up. "I've got to go to Joseph," he repeated almost impatiently, as if to stop all the talk of long preparations.

As he stood up, his sons surprisingly, alarmingly parted before him, scattered. There—wheeling and storming down Joseph's hill—came an Egyptian chariot, came Benjamin in the chariot. He swept to a halt before Jacob, stood in small-brother, excited pride, showing off Joseph's chariot to his father. "Joseph sent it for you, Father. They let me drive it all the way home, but I hid it behind the hill. Look at it—a real Egyptian chariot, and it's Joseph's!"

Jacob looked at Benjamin, looked at the chariot, wept, unashamed. "It is enough, and more than I deserve. God is good," he wept. He stepped to the chariot as if ready that moment to go with his youngest son to Egypt. Oh, he was ready—whatever preparations still had to be made—he was ready to leave starved Canaan, go to Egypt, go to Joseph.

The horses were champing at the bit, snorting. Benjamin was almost snorting and champing himself. "Let me take you around the tents," he begged. "Can I, Father? Just around the tents—I'll go awfully slow."

Jacob smiled, mounted the chariot, laid both his hands on Benjamin's shoulders to steady himself for the ride and to be very close to his youngest son who had come back to him.

Benjamin was back, Simeon was back, and Joseph was back from the dead—Joseph was alive.

"Yes, Bennie," he said softly. "Take me around the tents, Bennie. But not too wild, not too wild. . . ."

And Benjamin in his pride whooped with delight and yelled to the horses.

THE MAN OF GOD— THE MIRACLE MAN

And Israel dwelt in the land of Egypt, and grew and multiplied exceedingly.

And the time drew near that Jacob must die: and he called his son Joseph, and said unto him, "Bury me not in Egypt. But I will lie with my fathers, and thou shalt carry me out of Egypt and bury me in their burying place."

And his sons did unto him according as he had commanded them: for his sons carried him into the land of Canaan, and buried him in the cave of Machpelah. . . . And Joseph returned into Egypt, he, and his brethren, and all that went up with him to bury his father.

And Joseph dwelt in Egypt, he, and his father's house: and Joseph lived a hundred and ten years. And Joseph said unto his brethren, "I die: and God will surely bring you out of this land unto the land which he swore to Abraham, Isaac, and to Jacob." And Joseph took an oath of the children of Israel, saying, "God will surely visit you, and ye shall carry up my bones from hence." So Joseph died, and they embalmed him, and he was put in a coffin in Egypt.

Now there arose up a new king over Egypt, which knew not Joseph. And he said unto his people, "Behold, the people of Israel are mightier than we. Come on, let us deal wisely with them."

Therefore they did set over them taskmasters to afflict them with burdens. But the more they afflicted them, the more they multiplied and grew. And the Egyptians made the children of Israel to serve with rigor: and they made their lives bitter with hard bondage, in mortar, and in brick, and in all manner of service.

From GENESIS 47 & 50 *and* EXODUS 1

WHEN Jacob had died in Egypt, and his sons—Joseph and his brothers—had buried him in his own land of Canaan, Joseph's brothers had gone back to live in the province of Goshen which Joseph had provided for them, but Joseph had remained at Pharaoh's court to be vice-regent of Egypt for the rest of his life. Then Joseph, too, had died.

After Joseph's death, Joseph's brothers and Joseph's two sons, Ephraim and Manasseh, had stayed on in Goshen. There in Goshen, as the years multiplied into centuries, the sons of Jacob and Joseph had multiplied into twelve tribes, each tribe named after a son of Jacob or Joseph. The whole twelve tribes had become a nation, known as Israel.

But the Israelites had become a nation of slaves. The descendants of Jacob and Joseph had been made slaves to the Egyptians by the Egyptians.

Now after the centuries only the slave people of Israel in the province of Goshen still remembered the great Joseph. In Goshen, Joseph's bones waited among them for deliverance from Egypt. In the royal coffin the embalmed mummy of Joseph waited with the people of Israel for the return to their own land of Canaan—the land of their forefathers, Abraham, Isaac, and Jacob.

The great Joseph, vice-regent of all Egypt, had believed in his day that his brothers, or, surely, their descendants would someday return to Canaan—he had commanded them that his bones should not remain in Egypt. But over the centuries only the slave people of Israel still remembered it.

The Egyptians, whom Joseph once had saved from starvation in the great, long-ago, seven-year famine, had forgotten Joseph and his deeds. Joseph had died, the Pharaoh, under whom Joseph had served as vice-regent of Egypt, had died. New Pharaohs had come to the throne of Egypt.

The new Pharaohs had forgotten Joseph, but they had taken note of the rich cattle lands of Goshen that the Hebrew Joseph had given to his brothers and their descendants. They had taken note that through the years these foreigners in Goshen always multiplied and grew stronger. To prevent the Israelites from getting stronger and more numerous than the Egyptians, the Pharaohs had begun to oppress the people of Israel.

Each succeeding Pharaoh suppressed each succeeding generation of Israelites more cruelly, until at last they had made them total slaves. The slave people of Israel had been set to making bricks. Then, with the bricks they had made, they had to build whole cities for the Egyptians. And the years rolled on into long centuries of total slavery.

It must now be some forty years ago the cruelest Pharaoh of all had come to the throne. From the palace of this Pharaoh had come the most ruthless and vicious decree of all—the boy babies of the slave people of Israel were to be destroyed as soon as they were born. The Egyptians hadn't been able to kill off the slaves with the endless work of brickmaking, therefore this new Pharaoh had decided that to kill the boy babies was the horribly efficient way to hold down the numbers of the ever-multiplying slaves.

The Israelite slaves had had to submit to the horror. They had submitted to it for forty years now. The day the decree had been issued there had been a rebellious muttering of the men slaves, and a horrible soft keening of all the slave mothers, but the muted rebellion had gone down in numbed anguish. The decree of the Pharaoh had stood. That was forty years ago. The decree of Pharaoh still stood—the Hebrew boy babies were still being destroyed as fast as they were born—as fast as the Egyptians could find them.

Oh, there was a forty-year-old tale—just as old as the cruel decree—that some slave mother forty years ago had defied Pharaoh. Instead of killing the boy baby born to her, she had set him adrift in a little reed basket in the back waters of the River Nile. The way this old slave tale went, Pharaoh's daughter had then happened to come to the river to bathe, had heard a baby crying, had spied the basket, and had taken the baby out of the river and to her home to become her son. Eventually he grew up to become—of course, that was the whole point of the slave story—a ruler of Egypt. Then—powerful like the great Joseph of old—he would deliver his people from Egypt and from slavery.

Well, maybe it all had happened that way. But if it had, what in forty years had become of it? Always there were these wistful tales going the rounds of the huts in the slave quarters of Goshen. The tales were really nothing but the hope of Israel that someday someone would come to take the place of Joseph and deliver his people. The hopeful tale of the Nile water baby of forty years ago had gone the way of all such stories—it had become a dead hope. But the slave people had to have their stories and their memories to give them hope.

But here now—after forty years—the story of the Hebrew water baby who had become a ruler in the palace of the Pharaohs had suddenly sprung into life again. Once more, as it had forty years before, the story was going the rounds of the slave quarters. Somebody must have thought up something nice and hopeful to add. The story was that the water baby had actually grown up in Pharaoh's palace, just like any royal Egyptian. But then—ah, blood was thicker than Nile water—forty years old now, the Nile foundling had one day taken a stroll outside the royal gardens, and had seen an Egyptian belaboring a poor Israelite slave with a big bull whip. On the spot he had smashed down the Egyptian—killed him! And then he had fled into the wilderness.

The great man, the deliverer—who was to come out of the palace of Pharaoh, like the great Joseph of old—hadn't brought deliverance. Moses had killed one mean Egyptian, and then he had run like any defenseless slave. The adopted son of Pharaoh's daughter had fled from the palace, fled from Egypt, into the wilderness. And why not? What else could Moses have done? For all his fine clothes and fine palaces and royal manners, he was still nothing but a lowly, unspeakable Hebrew—one of the abominable slave people. The man couldn't have done anything but run. There was no hope. And no deliverance.

No hope.

Moses had killed one Egyptian, and the years went on again—forty more senseless, cruel years. To the faint memories of the long-ago Joseph was added the faint tale of the water baby placed in a basket in the River Nile, and the tale of Moses, the adopted son of Pharaoh's daughter, who had smitten down one lone Egyptian. But now that story of the murdered Egyptian was also already forty years old. The years went on, and the slavery. Still the slave people passed the old tales of greatness from mouth to mouth, and from generation to generation. It was all they had. How else might dumb slaves, who could neither read nor write, remember? A few old tales of remembered greatness, a coffin with a few old bones—it was all they had. All else was work and suffering and death.

More and more as the years rolled on the memory of their ancient forefathers in the land of Canaan, and the memory of their God and his promises, began dimming in the slave people's minds. They hardly remembered their own God. They served the gods and idols of the Egyptians—there was a powerful people, so their gods must be powerful gods. What better could a slave people do than to serve the same gods? It was far better than to hang on to old dead hopes.

But now here—this day—in spite of everything—once more the story of Moses was springing into life. Once more the persistent story of Moses began making the rounds, forty years after he'd killed the Egyptian and fled to the wilderness. Forty years. Well, after forty years in the wilderness, the water baby must now be eighty years old! Just the same, the new story this day was that Moses had come back to Egypt.

. . . Better the slaves rest for the coming backbreaking day—the days so hard, the nights so short—than to sit around in the dark of their slave huts all the long tired evening whispering the hopeful story—Moses is back!

Why had Moses come back after staying scared for forty years after killing one lone Egyptian? Of course, to deliver his people! Of course, what else? The fantastic hope always managed to leap to life again. It flamed in the eyes of those who told the story of Moses' return. It flickered like a little thin flame in the dark, unlighted slave quarters.

The new tale of hope, the rumor that Moses was back, died as it rose. It went down in new cruelty. An order came from the reigning Pharaoh. The unbelievable order met the slave workers as they trudged from their huts to the brick kilns of Egypt. The Egyptian overseers and whipmasters were only too willing to spell out the new order for the slaves: "Hear this, slaves! This is the order of Pharaoh, and this his royal decree: 'Make brick! Make just as many bricks as yesterday and the day before, but without straw. Go hunt the straw yourselves, then still make the same amount of bricks as was required of you when we furnished the straw.' "

This was impossible—it couldn't be done! This was insane! Pharaoh must have gone mad—this went too far in impossible cruelty even for a Pharaoh. Bricks without straw—it went beyond reason. They wouldn't do it! Among the brick kilns a brief slave rebellion flickered up. The rebellious slaves dared to appoint leaders. The appointed leaders took their lives in their hands, and formed a delegation to demand of the Egyptians why this new hardship had been loaded on them.

They were told. The Egyptian taskmasters seemed genuinely horrified; they were scandalized. "This Moses of yours," they told the humble slave delegation, "this erstwhile adopted son of Pharaoh's daughter came before Pharaoh—he and a brother of his named Aaron—and this Moses made demands of Pharaoh. Mind you, he, a Hebrew! He demanded to be allowed to lead you slaves into the wilderness on a three-day journey to worship your slave God. Just like that! But that always happens when you show a Hebrew kindness—they turn on you. This Moses may have been brought up in Pharaoh's palace, but just the same—once a slave, always a low-down slave. A Hebrew can't be trusted one kind moment."

The bowed delegation covertly looked at each other. Then Moses had come back! And he had actually dared to make demands of Pharaoh! Then this time it wasn't a slave-quarter rumor—a story. Oh, that man, Moses, must have courage.

"But why must we suffer for it?" the slave delegation meekly asked. "Why for what Moses did must we now make bricks without straw? We had nothing to do with it. We didn't ask to go sacrifice to our God; we worship your great gods."

The overseers shrugged it away. "Pharaoh has decided that if this Moses could make such demands, it must be that you slaves have so little work that you have time for travel and feasting and worshiping. So to take all such nonsense out of your heads, he has taken away your straw. . . . But who are you to question Pharaoh's decrees? Back to your work, slaves —and just as many bricks as before!"

With that the rebellion flickered out. It died in impatient grumbles—not against Pharaoh but against Moses. What possessed that man? Of all impossible requests to make—let slaves get out of sight and out of the country three days! Couldn't he have started with something much more reasonable? A three-day journey to sacrifice to their God! What God? They barely remembered a God of their own. He was the vague God of their ancient forefathers, who had made great promises to give them a land called Canaan, and to make of them and their descendants a great nation. Great nation! All He had made of them was a horde of helpless slaves, making brick without straw in a strange, cruel land.

It would have been better if they had never heard of this Moses, better his mother had drowned him in the Nile instead of disobeying the law. Nothing ever came of slave lawlessness but more cruelties. The Egyptians and their gods were all-powerful.

A wordless groaning went up that night from every hard cot in the slave huts of Goshen. A silent groaning that no one heard but the God of the slaves—the God they had long ago forgotten. And God remembered His people who in the centuries of slavery had all but forgotten Him. And God began to bring hope to His people.

The work of brickmaking had been made unbearably heavy by the Egyptians, but this miraculous day it almost seemed light. And after the long day of making brick without straw came the night, but there was no rest in the slave quarters of Goshen. The huts and the hovels seethed with talk. But these weren't rumors and wishful tales making the excited rounds of the slave quarters. This news came direct from the palace of Pharaoh. The slaves of Goshen told the news over and over, ran with it from hut to hut. Then all night long it was talked of in the dark quarters.

Moses—imagine it!—Moses had gone back to stand before Pharaoh and all his court. Moses and his brother, Aaron, had braved Pharaoh's wrath with the same demand—let my people go! Yes, demand! He hadn't asked—he'd told the all-powerful tyrant to let the slave people of Israel go.

Oh, didn't the man Moses have endless courage? But in a way he could have courage—in the forty years in the wilderness Moses had become a miracle man, and his brother Aaron with him. They'd learned magic in the wilderness. Of course, Pharaoh had refused Moses' second demand to let the slave people go. Moses had simply turned to Aaron, and he'd told his brother, "Throw your shepherd's staff on the floor right before Pharaoh's feet."

As that staff had landed, it had changed before Pharaoh's eyes—Aaron's staff had changed into a writhing, hissing, curling snake! It had even forced Pharaoh to pull his feet up under him on the seat of the throne—to get his bare sandaled toes away from the serpent!

There was whispered laughter this night in the dark slave quarters of Goshen—the slave people laughing about mighty Pharaoh.

But the next day there came the crushing news—Pharaoh's court magicians had also performed the miracle of the snakes. Their canes when they tossed them on the ground had also changed to snakes. Later the story went the rounds that Aaron's staff had changed into a bigger snake, and Aaron's snake had swallowed up the cane snakes of Pharaoh's magicians. Ah, poor people, always they had to embroider these tales—somebody must have added a little bright something to give himself a bit of hope, and now everybody hopefully repeated it. Well, it was the only way perhaps that poor dumb slaves could get away from the raw truth staring them in the face—if Pharaoh's magicians could do what Moses and Aaron did, then the lives of Moses and Aaron weren't worth an Egyptian penny. If Moses' magic wasn't greater than the magic of Egypt, if Moses couldn't perform bigger, stronger, blacker magic—then Moses was doomed, and they all were doomed to eternal slavery.

And there went their hope. It was such a small hope. It was all centered on one man, Moses. One man alone against the Egyptians. One man with nothing but a shepherd's staff in his hand going before the all-powerful Pharaoh in the name of the Lord God of Israel—a slave god of a slave people. Ah, wasn't it a hopeless hope?

But hope leaped the next day. The slaves were summoned by the desperate Egyptians. They were marched away from their brick kilns and buildings and hurriedly set to dig wells. Wells had to be dug all along the Nile. Moses, the man of God, the miracle man, had performed the greatest magic ever heard of—he had turned water to blood. At his word all the water in Egypt had changed into blood. The rivers floated with dead fish, the rivers stank with fish floating in blood, and the Egyptians were dying of thirst. The slaves were set to dig new wells for clear, pure, colorless water—all else was blood. The Nile flowed blood.

The slaves dug the wells joyfully—almost willingly, but not too fast. It was good to see the Egyptians suffer in their turn—let them suffer—don't dig too fast, let their tongues hang out. . . . But the well digging was stopped almost as it began. Pharaoh's magicians had once more matched the magic of Moses—they, too, could make water turn to blood. The disturbed, defeated slaves went back to their brick kilns and building and the hopeless scrounging for straw.

And then—hardly back at their kilns and their bricks—the slaves were once more summoned and sent out through all Egypt. Now it was frogs—not blood, frogs! It was as if this time at the word of Moses every drop of water in Egypt had changed into a frog. Millions of frogs, a hundred million upon a hundred million, frogs upon frogs, frogs piled on frogs. There couldn't be that many frogs in all the earth, but they were in Egypt—in the houses, in the beds, in the food, and in the baths. The slaves made chortling jokes to each other about the great ladies of Egypt bathing in frogs. They pictured them sitting in the water of their tubs, and suddenly the water was frogs. Frogs under them, frogs over them, squirming cold green frogs around them to the bathtub's rim.

The Egyptians locked themselves in their houses. Nothing moved, nothing stirred but frogs. The frogs and long slave columns squashing down the roads to clean up the frog mess for the Egyptians. Then the silent, secret laughter of the slaves at the distress of their masters, the Egyptians, died in them. Word came—Pharaoh's magicians had also performed the miracle of bringing up frogs.

The frogs died, the jokes and the hopes of the Israelites died, but they still had to perform the grim, glum, onerous chore of gathering the dead frogs and heaping them in piles. The land was heaped with frogs, but the great plague was over, and it had accomplished nothing—nothing. As soon as Pharaoh found that his own magicians could perform the magic of Moses, he would not let the slave people go—not for three days, not for a moment. The iron-willed Pharaoh did not stand in a bit of dread of the God of Israel and his miracle man, Moses. And why should he, if Moses' magic wasn't any stronger than the magic of the court magicians?

The slaves were still busy filling the wells they had begun to dig with the bodies of the dead frogs when the news of the third plague came. Lice! The slaves learned of it in their land of Goshen in the morning—only because no Egyptian came to summon them and march them off to work. The news of the third plague ran like a brush fire through the slave quarters and villages of Goshen. Lice—this time it was lice. Lice, then lice and more lice. And all Moses had done was to hit the ground before Pharaoh with his staff. Some of the slaves running from hut to hut with the news insisted Moses hadn't even bothered to do as much as that—he'd just told his brother Aaron to strike the ground before Pharaoh's feet. Anyway—lice—a puff of lice from that little puff of dust spurting up around the staff as it hit the ground. Then lice thick as dust everywhere, no, dust changing into lice. Lice filled the earth and sky. Lice covered the land—the land crawled. Lice over Egypt, lice on the people and on the animals, lice in and on and over everything. It was so terrible that everything had stopped in Egypt. The Egyptians couldn't move, couldn't work, couldn't even work the slaves for lice. For the first time in the centuries the Israelite slaves in Goshen had a free day. No one came to march them to work.

The slaves waited in their quarters, trembling with anticipation. Surely the free day was a sign, surely after this, as soon as he could send messengers through the lice, Pharaoh would send word that he was letting the Israelites go.

No royal messengers came. Word came that the court magicians had not been able to perform this third magic miracle of Moses. The word was that the magicians themselves crawled with lice, the magicians were cowering under the lice. The magicians might be terrified, but not Pharaoh. The iron-willed, pigheaded Pharaoh backed down for nothing, and no messengers came.

The slaves waited in Goshen, the paralyzed land waited for the lice to go, and at last the lice went. But almost as the lice went the flies came. For the fourth time Moses had gone before Pharaoh, and now at Moses' word came the pest of flies. The land of Egypt became a black land, black with flies. The Egyptians couldn't move for flies, couldn't eat, couldn't open their mouths to breathe.

But this fourth miracle was a miracle of miracles. It was a

miracle within a miracle—there wasn't a fly in the filthy, cramped, overcrowded slave quarters of Goshen—not a fly more than ordinary in Goshen. Did Pharaoh know? Did he know that in the slaves' quarters the air was clean and blue and bright, while all Egypt reeked and was corrupt with flies? But a miracle within a miracle—that could not be merely the magic of Moses—this was the work of Moses' God and of their God! Their God had set his people apart. Now even the pigheaded Pharaoh must acknowledge that the God of the slaves was greater than all Pharaohs and all magicians and all gods.

But when the great news came, even though the slaves had breathlessly awaited it after this miracle within a miracle, it was so great it was unbelievable. What the blood and frogs and lice had failed to accomplish, the horror of flies had forced on Pharaoh. Pharaoh had called Moses before him and had told Moses to take the slaves into the wilderness to worship and sacrifice—but not to go very far. Even so, this was the first chink in the armor of Pharaoh, the first ray of hope in the long centuries of slavery.

The excited slave people trembled. In the great new expectation they kept telling each other the great good news over and over, so that in the telling they could believe it themselves, make it real, make it believable—get themselves used to the unbelievable.

Ah, but the man Moses was too merciful! He hadn't suffered as they had all the years under the hard, merciless hands of the Egyptians. At the promise of Pharaoh to let the slaves go, Moses had immediately called off the pestilence of flies. The flies had gone in a buzzing, roaring black mass over the Red Sea and the wilderness, but with the flies went Pharaoh's promise. He would not let the slave people go—not even for three days, not even for a short distance.

Hope died. What would it take to change the stubborn, heartless Pharaoh? If he had a heart, it was a heart of stone. The Egyptian people were changing, the tormented, scared Egyptians were eager to see the slaves go, but they had nothing to say. Only Pharaoh was all-powerful.

Hope died, hope leaped. It was hard to change so fast—so fast the plagues now came over Egypt. In the first night that Egypt was free of the flies, the cattle of the Egyptians died. But not a rattleboned, half-starved cow died in Goshen. Not a cow nor a calf. Couldn't Pharaoh see? Wouldn't he see? Didn't he know now that the God of Moses and the God of the Israelites was mightier than all Pharaohs and all gods?

The cows died and lay dead on all the hills. The cows lay bloating in the sweltering heat, undisturbed and unvisited, for hard upon the plague of death for the cattle had come the plague of boils on the Egyptian people. Pharaoh—even Pharaoh—was covered with boils. In the midst of the torment and hideous repulsiveness of boils the land of Egypt began to swelter in the pressure and foreboding of a ghastly still-standing heat—the oppressive heat that foretells the coming of terrible storms. The cows lay dead in the heat, but the Egyptians had to stand. They were unable to sit, unable to lie, unable to stand the pressure and friction of clothes on their boils. To the torment of the boils was still added the corroding, gnawing sting of salt sweat in the boils. It drove the people out of their sweltering houses to find a little relief, a breath of air. But into the plague of boils came the next plague.

The ghastly heat boiled into a storm. In the midst of the heat hail, cold, hard hail, lashed down on the naked people and their boils. Hail smashed down the roofs of their houses, as if still to get at the people when they fled inside their houses. Then amidst the cold, merciless rain there came a crashing of thunder and lightning. There didn't seem room in the sky for all the hail and thunder and lightning. Down it came on the screaming, naked people and their boils.

But not a hailstone fell in Goshen. In Goshen there was only the crashing roar of the thunder and the sight of lightning as it smashed down from the sky amongst the hail. Outside the borders of Goshen the thunder and lightning sizzled along the roads and flamed along the rooftops, but Goshen lay still. The land of Egypt all around was a fuming sulphurous hell of fire, but Goshen lay still.

The storm had to end or nothing would have stood, nothing in Egypt would have come out alive. But, no, the storm it seemed had ended only to make room for the next terrible plague, since the next plague could not have gone on among hail and fire and thunder. After the lightning and the thunder came locusts, came a thunder of locusts. The locusts came roaring up out of the wilderness in such multitudes that their wings roared in the sky that their bodies darkened. The locusts came down into the flattened emptiness that the hail and the fire and the destruction had left. They came down to eat it. What the hail and fire had spared the locusts consumed.

Not a locust came down in Goshen. Not a green sprig in Goshen was devoured, not even a stalk of dead straw trodden into the ground by slave feet. Outside the borders of Goshen the Israelites could hear the locusts eating. They stood appalled at the tearing, chewing, sawing, unending sound—the sound of insects eating up a land.

What went on in that Pharaoh's mind? Was he going to wait until nothing was left? But Pharaoh waited, and a wind came up and blew the locusts over the Red Sea. They drowned in the sea. It was said that the Red Sea had turned green with floating locusts. It was said that locusts had filled the ships on the sea, and had sunk the ships. It was said . . . But the locusts were gone, and again, with the plague gone, Pharaoh refused to let the slave people of Israel go.

The slaves said among themselves that Moses was far too merciful. He should have let the locusts stay. How many times hadn't it happened now? Eight times, eight plagues? The moment Moses called off a plague, Pharaoh set his heart like a rock, brought down the hammer of his iron will, and refused to let the Israelites go. What did it have to take to change Pharaoh's mind? What could there be left in plagues and torment?

The ninth plague when it came seemed too merciful to the slaves. Darkness—only darkness—but complete, utter, immovable darkness. After the horrible sound of the eating of the locusts, there stood the silence of total darkness. It was a darkness so thick, so dense, so impenetrable, it rose like a towering black wall high as the sky—so high it must reach to the heavens and to God. The wall of blackness rose into the sky from the exact borders of Goshen. Goshen lay like an island of light and sun and air in the midst of an Egyptian darkness towering up all around the slave land. The darkness was so immense, so solid, it seemed to the slave people in the light as if they could lean against the wall of darkness, push against it, and that to penetrate it they would have had to hack into it with axes.

Three days and three nights Egypt lay in the darkness. But to the disappointed slaves this ninth plague seemed merciful—a merciful blotting out for the Egyptians of death and destruction and emptiness after the hail and the fire and the locusts.

In their light land with the sun warm in a blueness and brightness of sky the slave people waited, but without hope. If all the other plagues had accomplished nothing, what could the black silence in Egypt accomplish? Hope had leaped and hope had died eight times now—the slaves waited, and everything around them waited. The world stood still in an immovableness of darkness.

The third day of the blackness messengers came. They came plunging, they came stumbling; some came crawling on hands and knees from out of the wall of black into the pool of light that was the land of Goshen. And every one of the messengers stood for a moment speechless and blinded and awed in the sudden freedom of light and air. The messengers had come out of black Egypt, but these messengers were not from Pharaoh. These were messengers sent by Moses. Swift runners from Moses. The orders came direct from Moses to his people. The messengers ran with the news, they shouted the orders, went with them to all the slave villages and quarters of Goshen. They called and shouted the loud news into every mean street and down every alley.

"Get ready! This is the order of Moses and of your God! Stand ready at midnight. Knead unleavened dough, and wrap both the dough and your kneading troughs in a cloth and sling it over your shoulders, and stand ready.

"Stand ready, but stay in your houses. Not a man, woman, or child must go out of your huts until morning light. After you've kneaded your dough, and before you shut yourselves inside your houses, do this—take blood, paint blood on the lintels and sides of your doors. Do not fail! Not a single house must fail in this, for at midnight the avenging angel will pass through the land of Egypt, and through the land of Goshen —people of Israel, your God is coming to you. But if in any of your houses the door is not sprinkled with blood—in that house the firstborn shall die. But if the door is sprinkled with blood, the avenging angel of the Lord God of Israel will pass over that house—not a soul shall die in that house.

"Everywhere else, all over Egypt, the firstborn of the people and the firstborn of the animals down to the lowliest dog in the street shall die. It shall come about at midnight! And a wailing and screaming of sorrow and death shall rise up from Egypt. But do not move from your houses, do not open your doors, but stand ready behind your closed doors, for this time Pharaoh and his people will not merely let you go—they will push you out of Egypt."

It had come! And now it was awesome. After centuries of slavery suddenly had come their deliverance from Egypt. Awed, silent, the slave people listened to the orders shouted over and over. They mumbled it over and over to themselves and to each other. It had come. God had come to them, and freedom had come, for He was their God. He was not merely the God of Moses, the miracle man—but He was also their great God, and He had come to them.

Death came at midnight. Death entered every house in Egypt, death came to the firstborn of Pharaoh, who was to inherit the throne. Death went down every road into every house. Death found the firstborn of the scrawniest cat in the narrowest squeeze of hidden alleys. It came to the firstborn of rats and mice under the floors of the houses. The firstborn scorpion hidden in the thatch dropped down dead to the trodden earthen floor. Death found the firstborn adder coiled in a cup of dust at the side of a pitted road. And silently the adder died at that midnight moment.

Death came to all the firstborn in the land of Egypt at that same midnight moment, and the land screamed with horror and terror and sorrow. The screaming of sorrow was so terrible that the slave people in their shut-up houses had to remember not to open the doors—had to remember that these were the Egyptians who had forced them without any pity to kill off their boy babies when they were born. Now death had come to the Egyptians, and Goshen stayed silent and shut.

In the morning with the dawning of the first little rift of gray light there came a pounding and hammering and knocking on all the closed doors of the huts and hovels in Goshen. The Egyptians had come out to their slaves. And as doors opened to them, the red-eyed, broken, hopeless Egyptians pleaded with the slaves, begged their slaves to get out of the land. Wordless with sorrow, they shoved food and jewelry and money and clothing at the slaves. They thrust it at them; they threw it at them. "Go. Oh, go. Get out of Egypt before we are all destroyed."

The slaves went, for they were ready. They left at the moment. Having waited through hopeless centuries, through all the years and the generations, they were ready—oh, they were ready. Ready to be slaves no longer—ready to be free.

The mass of slaves marched silently, urgently—the men, the women, the children, and all their animals—the Israelites and all they possessed. From every byway, street, and crooked alley little silent files of people streamed out to join the columns marching down the roads. And the columns on the roads merged into a mighty torrent and a surge of people, all going down the main road leading out of Egypt to the wilderness. It was like a mighty river surging toward the sea—a river of people—a people surging toward their freedom. Six hundred thousand hurrying, silent people almost desperately rushing out of Egypt toward their freedom. It couldn't be believed, it couldn't be expressed; they could only rush on.

Fast and silent as they strode, the Egyptians still kept running out to the line of march, ran along the line of march, shoving food and clothing and gifts at the slaves. "Get out. Get out. Oh, please get out."

The surging columns still combined and flowed together until all were massed on the wilderness road. The tight mass rushed on as they followed Moses, who somewhere unseen and far up ahead was leading his people out of Egypt. They followed the coffin with the bones of Joseph—far ahead and unseen—the bones that had waited with them through the centuries for this deliverance.

Oh, Joseph had believed, and Moses had believed, and now they too believed in the greatness of their God, for they were marching on the road to freedom. Ah, the bones of Joseph were moving on to the promised land. And they, the people, were on their way to the promised land. They marched, a nation of slaves, to become a nation of free men in the land promised them by their God. Their Great God, who had promised it, and now had brought it about. They were marching on to freedom. They were free. Ah, they were free!

PART IV

A LAND
FOR
A NATION

GIANTS IN THE LAND

And the people removed from Hazeroth, and pitched in the wilderness of Paran.

And the Lord spoke unto Moses, saying, "Send thou men, that they may search the land of Canaan, which I give unto the children of Israel."

And Moses sent them to spy out the land of Canaan, and said unto them, "Get you up this way southward, and go out into the mountain: and see the land, what it is; and the people that dwelleth therein, whether they be strong or weak, few or many; and what the land is that they dwell in, whether it be good or bad; and what cities they be that they dwell in, whether in tents, or in strongholds: and what the land is, whether it be fat or lean. . . . And be ye of good courage, and bring of the fruit of the land."

Now the time was the time of the first ripe grapes. . . .

Now after the death of Moses it came to pass that the Lord spoke unto Joshua, Moses' minister, saying, "Moses my servant is dead; now therefore arise, go over this Jordan, thou, and all this people, unto the land which I do give them, even to the children of Israel. Every place that the sole of your foot shall tread upon, that have I given unto you, as I said unto Moses. From the wilderness and this Lebanon even unto the great river, the river Euphrates . . . and unto the great sea toward the going down of the sun shall be your coast. Be strong and of good courage: for unto this people shalt thou divide for an inheritance the land, which I swore unto their fathers to give them."

And Joshua sent out two men to spy secretly, saying, "Go view the land, even Jericho."

From NUMBERS 12 & 13 *and* JOSHUA 1 & 2

NOW after the horrible journey through desert and wasteland from Egypt to Canaan, Moses had at last led the Israelites up to the borders of the promised land. The wilderness wandering hadn't merely been a journey through wasteland; it had been a journey to become a nation under the leadership of the great Moses. A nation of free men instead of a nation of disorganized, undisciplined slaves.

Moses had not merely led them, he had taught and instructed them, shown them how to become a nation, and govern themselves as a free nation. Moses had told them about God. The great God of Israel and his great promises, the memory of which had all but dimmed out in the four centuries of slavery in Egypt. He had shown them how to worship their one God—one nation, one God.

Now they stood at the borders of Canaan. They were a free nation, but still dispossessed—Canaan still had to be conquered. But now they had their leaders, their captains, and their armies; they had their priests and princes, their governors and their laws. They had their great leader, Moses. They had everything a free nation of free people must have to stay free. All they lacked was a land. It lay before them.

From the wilderness they looked out at Canaan. This was the land of their fathers, where in the ancient days Abraham, Isaac, and Jacob had lived. It was theirs to take, to conquer and possess.

As the first step in the conquest of Canaan, Moses had sent out twelve spies to search out the strength and the weaknesses of the land. Forty days the spies had been gone, but now from the outposts of the wilderness camp word had come—the spies were approaching the camp. Twelve had been sent out, all twelve were making their way back. The whole camp streamed out to meet the spies. Everybody was eager to know about Canaan. It was in the time of the first ripe grapes. A beautiful time, a hopeful time. The whole desert camp was eager about Canaan.

There they came—the first two spies. There they came, not creeping or skulking, but walking bold and tall—as if they'd come from raiding an orchard—instead of from a forty-day dangerous mission of spying out a whole hostile land. But the two spies had to walk tall, if only to keep what ever they were carrying between them from dragging over the ground. They were carrying something from a pole slung over their shoulders. Was it? . . . It couldn't be! But it was—it was a branch with a cluster of grapes so huge that it had to be carried from a pole on the men's shoulders. Out of the dry land the desert dwellers stared with greedy eyes at the giant cluster of grapes. Now, two by two, more spies approached the wilderness camp. And these, too, were carrying fruit—grapes, pomegranates, figs—luscious ripe fruit, dripping with goodness! Surely Canaan must be an unbelievably rich, good land to grow such fruit!

It was a good land, the first two spies reported as soon as the babbling people, crowding about them and plucking at the cluster of grapes, would listen and let them be heard. It was an unbelievably rich land. Unfortunately, the land of

Canaan did not only grow giant clusters of grapes, it also grew giants. The two spies had seen giants in the land of Canaan —men so huge that the spies had not dared to come anywhere near them. Again and again they had seen giants walking in towering strength, and even though they'd only seen them from a distance, the spies by comparison had looked like grasshoppers in size. Yes, grasshoppers!

There were giants in Canaan, and great walled cities. All the cities were surrounded with enormously high, stout walls. In the four centuries that the Israelites had been slaves in Egypt, the people who had taken over Canaan had grown mighty and powerful—Canaan was unbeatable. And then there were the giants!

The dumbfounded, dismayed people looked at the other spies who had come up to stand quietly behind the first two spies with the grapes—tired and dispirited. They didn't say much, these others—just agreed there wasn't a chance. Not a chance! Not against walled cities and giants.

Uncomfortably the people looked from the fruit to the quiet, tired men. They waited silently—the last two spies were just now coming up. There they came—Caleb and Joshua—the youngest of the twelve. "Well, what do you two say? What do you think about it?"

"About what?"

"About those giants and walled cities?"

"You told them that?" Caleb's mouth hung open as he stared at the ten silent men. He turned to the people. "There are giants, and there are walled cities," he said quietly. "But, at least, let's try it. We can overcome them."

The crowd turned on Joshua. "And you—what do you say?"

"There are some giants and some walled cities, but there is also milk and honey, and fruit and every kind of goodness. And Caleb is right. We can do it. We've got to do it—it's an exceedingly good land. And if God is with us, He will give us the victory."

At Joshua's word about milk and honey, the people looked at the grapes and the pomegranates and figs, and their mouths watered. Then they looked at the other spies, and the ten tired men shook their heads. And at that the hearts of the people seemed to turn to water. They, too, became afraid. They still wavered, but then some began to mutter. Somebody in the back ranks shouted out against Joshua. Suddenly the people rebelled, suddenly fear made them rebel, and all in one moment they turned viciously on Joshua and Caleb.

Joshua and Caleb stood tall and still in the midst of the crowd. The crowd began picking up stones. The milling crowd began screaming at Joshua and Caleb about finding themselves new leaders—new leaders, in the place of Moses and Aaron, who would lead them back to Egypt. Anything was better than this fearsomeness. Anything! Even slavery was better! Their fathers had at least been fed regularly by the Egyptians—maybe only to get more work out of them—but at least they'd had homes and food and protection. They didn't have to break down walls and smite down giants. Away with Moses—away with Aaron—stone those two reckless young spies! We want new leaders to lead us back to Egypt.

Turn back! Turn back! Go back to Egypt and to safety.

Safety! Ah, they'd been made free men, but they still had the hearts of slaves and not of free men.

Before any stones could fly, into the midst of the screaming, howling, hysterical, rebellious mob marched Moses, gray of hair and grim of face. The crowd fell back before him, stood aside until Moses stood with Caleb and Joshua, facing the frightened, hushed mob.

"Hear the word of the Lord who led you out of Egypt," Moses sternly told his people. "There will be no turning back to Egypt. You will not go back to Egypt—but you will go back into this wilderness. Your bones will bleach in the wilderness. Forty days the ten cowardly spies were in promised Canaan, for forty years you will not enter Canaan. For each day the spies had in that land of milk and honey, you will spend a year in this dry, empty desert. Forty years until you die—all you slavish, rebelling wretches and your ten craven spies. All, except Caleb and Joshua."

The word of the Lord had come to His people, and Moses, who had led his people to the promised land, now had to lead them back into the wilderness. The Israelites withdrew from Canaan back into the wilderness—back into the hopelessness, back into the ruggedness to teach a new generation, still to come up, courage and strength—teach them to be a free nation, free of fear, trusting in their God.

Canaan had to wait forty years for a new generation to be born and to grow up. Canaan had lain ripe before them in the promising time of the first ripe grapes, but it had to wait forty years for a new people with a new courage and a newborn trust in their God.

Now they were all dead—the whole generation—even Moses their great leader had died. He had once led his people up to the promised land, but they hadn't dared, they'd rebelled, and with them he'd turned back into the wilderness to teach them to be a God-fearing nation—one nation, with one God, and one faith in their God. Moses had died without entering the promised land. He had seen Canaan, but he had not entered it.

Now it was up to Joshua and Caleb, the only two left of the cowardly, rebellious generation—the only two who had not feared great walls and huge giants. Once more Israel was back at the borders of Canaan, but now the host stood at the banks of the Jordan. Beyond Jordan lay Canaan. Once again, after forty long years, spies were sent out, but now Joshua was careful to send not twelve, but only two spies into Canaan. Only two spies to spy out only one town—Jericho—the first walled stronghold that lay across Israel's path of conquest beyond the River Jordan.

But now it wasn't the time of the first ripe grapes as it had been forty years before. Now it was the time of the full harvest. The time when the Jordan overflowed all its banks. The two young spies swam the swollen river, crawled up the opposite bank, and disappeared from sight. Again the host of Israel waited for the return of its spies.

This time the army of Israel waited impatiently. This army had been tried in battle. They had fought the Amalakites and the Midianites this side of Jordan, and had won great victories. These were battle-tried soldiers—warriors—and after forty years of hardships and training in the wilderness they felt ready and able to cross into Canaan and conquer the promised land.

Three days the camp of Israel waited for the two spies. Something must have gone terribly wrong across Jordan—the spies should have been back long before this. The Israelites couldn't wait much longer. Every day Jordan was rising, every day it was becoming more impossible for the army to cross, let alone the women and children. The soldiers muttered amongst themselves. What was this delay? Why not at least send the army across and get on with it? Never mind the two spies, get on with it, take Canaan!

The two spies were in Jericho. They had managed, they thought, to steal unnoticed through the great iron gate in the wall. They had chosen the unguarded moment when the patrolling sentry had his mind and eyes on some girls taking an evening stroll on top of the wall near the gate. As the sentry tilted his head back and yelled something up at the girls, the spies hustled in through the gate. Behind them the girls on the wall giggled, made some silly answer to the sentry, and he had some more clever remarks to make to them. The spies slipped into Jericho.

As the two spies slid along the drab, dusky wall of a narrow alley, trying to work themselves unnoticed into the heart of the city, suddenly not far behind them they heard a roar and a rattle of chains. They pressed against the wall, listened. At first the sound baffled them, but then they puzzled it out—the great gate to the city was falling shut. That could only be for one of two reasons—darkness was coming and the time of the closing of gates, or they'd been seen!

The spies couldn't know. But they did know it was best not to go skulking around by alleys and byways, best not to stand there exposed against the bare, solid wall. It was best they move on, act casual and unhurried. The city wall loomed up at the far end of the alley in which the spies found themselves. The spies walked boldly down the middle of the alley to the city wall. They ascended a stairway of steps cut into the inner slope of the wall. They hurried across the top of the wall. With the gate closed, the only means of escape left to them would be to jump down the wall. But when the spies peered down the outside of the wall their hearts sank. To plunge down that wall was to plunge to their death—the wall was enormously high, much higher than it had looked on their stealthy approach to Jericho. It was breath-taking. Desperately the two spies looked in both directions along the wall. The wall was not only enormously high, it was broad as a street—broad enough for a house to stand on it. There was even a house built on top of this wall! Beyond them there it rose—a solitary house.

Suddenly the spies stood rigid. From down below in the street came the measured tread of marching soldiers. The night patrol, or searching parties? If one of the girls on the wall flirting with the gate sentry had happened to see the two spies slipping in through the gate, then the soldiers were now coming for them. And here on top of the wall, silhouetted against the evening sky, they two stood out like sentinels. Sentinels? The spies looked at each other meaningfully. Then, without a word, they, too, with measured steps—like sentries—marched boldly along the top of the wall toward the lone house on the wall.

In the shadows of the house they threw themselves flat, lay in long silence, listening for any sound from inside the house. There was no sound. If the house should be empty, if the house should happen to possess a coil of rope, there might still be a chance for escape. They would tie the rope somewhere to the part of the house jutting out over the wall, lower themselves by the rope, drop the rest of the way if necessary. . . . One of the spies carefully raised himself, tested the door. It was not locked. They eased the creaking door open. After a death-still wait they slipped inside the house.

There was no sound. Gradually the men's eyes grew accustomed to the deeper darkness inside—only a little light filtered through the one high window at the side of the room. Suddenly something stirred, something glinted. It was a woman. A woman was in the room. There stood a woman pressed against the far wall—the last sudden rays of a dying evening light had glinted briefly in her hair—red hair. Wordlessly the spies stared at the woman.

"Spies," the woman whispered hoarsely. "You're spies. From the camp of Israel, I know. So we are to be next. Jericho's next. We've heard what you did to the Midianites across Jordan, so now it's our turn." She was suddenly silent. She stood, head twisted, listening. Outside the silent house down below the wall there was a sound of running feet in the streets, guarded calls. . . . The two spies grimly advanced on the woman—all she'd have to do was let out one wild scream and the Jericho guard would come. Patrols must be moving in all the streets.

A board creaked in the silent house, and the woman turned back to the spies. "This house on the wall," she whispered hastily, "you did the right thing. They won't expect that you would dare to hide in the one house on the wall. But the town will be searched street by street and house by house, and when they don't find you down in the town they'll come here. . . . Well, there isn't any place to go from here—except—still higher. Up on the roof! Follow me up on the roof. I've got flax up there spread to dry—I'll hide you under the flax."

The spies had no choice. They had to trust her. They let her lead them to the roof, let her cover them with bundles of flax. There she left them.

Like cornered rats under straw, the two spies lay on the flat roof under the flax, listening to every sound down below them. They strained their ears for the creaking of the house door, but down below everything stayed quiet. The red-headed woman must be down there, watching and waiting—if she wasn't flashing a warning light to the searching parties down below in the town. But nothing happened, nothing developed. If it was a trap, the woman below was playing a waiting game. The house stayed silent, but outside the house the search was coming closer, now it was centering on the wall. There was the sound of marching, scuffling feet over the flat stone top of the wall. Then it came, and it stopped the hearts of the hidden spies—there it was at last, the heavy pounding on the door.

The spies had to lie there listening to the muffle and mumble of voices, then the woman's voice sharpened. "Sure, I saw the men! They came on the wall, but when they took one look over the wall they scuttled right back down into the town. . . . Spies?

"No, they were too far away, and it was getting dusky—I didn't suspect they were spies. I was busy spreading flax on the roof, I just happened to notice them, but I was busy and gave it no further thought. . . .

"No, they couldn't be here—wouldn't they be fools to pick a lone house on the wall? No, as I said it was getting dusky, but it was well before the time of the closing of the town gate—if you didn't find them down in the town, it seems to me you ought to look for them outside the town. They must have managed to get through the gate, and if they did they should be on their way back to their camp on the Jordan."

Was it a ruse? Was she, while she was talking, pointing up to the roof, making signs to the soldiers? She sounded almost too cool and calm. But there was no need for her to make secret signs. The two on the roof were helpless as mice.

The Jericho guard believed her! It must have seemed insane to them for spies to hide in a house on a wall. They didn't even ask to search. And the woman seemingly not hiding a single thing—coolly telling them she'd seen the spies, telling them she'd been spreading flax. . . . Ah, she was a cool one, she seemed to know how to handle men. There was a smothered laugh, the door closed, and the guard marched away along the wall.

Down below the house stayed silent a long time. Then at last the woman softly called to the two men. They stood before her again, down in the room, and she was waiting for them—ah, she was a cool one—she was waiting with a coil of rope in her hand. A bright red rope!

"I'm going to let you down the wall by this rope," she whispered to the men. "Right through the window. It's dark enough now so you won't be seen. And this house juts out over the wall, so as you slide down you'll be in the deep shadows. It's the darkest part of the wall; they won't see you from the watchtowers. . . . But slide smoothly, don't kick out or struggle. And hide in the hills on the other side of the town from Jordan. Don't try to make your way back to camp—I suspect the whole countryside is going to be searched. Hide in the hills for at least three days, then make your way back. But now you must hurry."

She tied the rope securely to a beam below the windowsill. Each spy in turn tested the rope and the knot, nodded approval.

"Now," the woman whispered. "But remember me when your armies come to take the town."

The first spy let himself out through the window down into the darkness. He slid from sight.

The rope slackened. Now the second spy stepped to the window.

"My name is Rahab," the red-haired woman said.

"Rahab! We'll remember you. But tell me, why did you

do this for us, when you just had to lift a finger to the guard?" The spy shoved himself backward through the window, hung over the sill, looked hard at the woman.

"Oh, don't you know? We've heard what the armies of Israel did to the Moabites and the Midianites across Jordan, and for all its walls Jericho stands in terror of Israel. That's why they searched so desperately for you. But remember me when you take the town."

The spy backed farther through the window, but still clung to the sill. "We'll remember, but we'll only be a small part of a big army. . . . This red rope. Hang a piece of it out of this window through which we escaped. And I swear, if the red rope is there, nothing shall happen to your red head."

There was an impatient yank on the rope from below. The spy immediately shoved himself through the window, and slid smoothly from the woman's sight.

At last the two spies were back with their tale of Rahab and of Jericho, a town in terror. At last Joshua had given the order to break camp and cross Jordan. In the early morning the whole camp was on the march, the columns of Israel moved slowly toward the swollen river. But of all things —not the captains, not the soldiers, but seven priests, carrying on their shoulders the sacred ark of the covenant, were sent out ahead of the line of march. At the order of Joshua they marched straight into the rushing river. The first priest took the first step into the water. Then, miracle of miracles, at the touch of the priest's foot the river stopped. The rushing river stopped, the water stopped! It stood still, it rose up in a wall, it piled up and backed up into an enormous wall of water with nothing holding it back—as if a great, unseen, mighty hand were pushing it back. The water stood as water stands behind a mighty dam, but there was no dam, there was nothing. There were only the seven priests in their long, flowing robes, dwarfed by the wall of water, marching solemnly to the middle of the dry river with the sacred ark of God.

Into the dry river marched the armies of Israel. Behind them the whole mass of people—the women and children, the old men and the animals, loaded with all their belongings—flowed down into the river in a tightly packed mass. The mass split into two columns in the middle of the river, flowed around the ark where it rested on dry river bottom with the seven priests standing tall and still beside it. The columns closed up again and marched on. Hour after hour the columns flowed down into the river, crossed the river, and climbed the far bank until the whole host had crossed Jordan, down to the last child and old man, and the last cat and dog and old cow.

In the middle of the river, behind the line of march, the seven priests took up the ark and carried it to the riverbank. Then, miracle of miracles, the moment the last priest pulled his foot from the water, the wall of water collapsed in a thundering, foaming roar, and mighty Jordan rushed on again, rolled on as it always had before.

It was an awesome sight, an awesome moment, but the

host of Israel could not stand still, it moved on toward Jericho. Somehow the mud and stone wall of Jericho did not seem very tremendous now after they'd seen the wall of water of their mighty God. Coolly, in sight of all Jericho, the Israelites made camp for the women and children and non-combatants. But the warriors did not stay. The moment camp had been made, they marched out to lay siege to walled Jericho. The women and children watched from the camp. The people of Jericho watched from the wall. The wall of Jericho was black with people.

There came the army of Israel, with Joshua at the head. The priests and the ark of the covenant came on behind the line of march. Seven priests with seven trumpets made of ram's horns marched out before the ark and the seven priests carrying the ark. The strange, silent siege of Jericho had begun.

Far out from the great wall the line of march wound around the town—far enough from the wall to be out of spear's throw and arrow range. The solemn, silent marching column did nothing but march—not a spear was raised, not as much as a fist was lifted. Only at one point where the Israelites passed the house built on top of the wall did the heads turn to look at the house with its piece of scarlet rope dangling from its one window. Otherwise the army of Israel completely ignored Jericho.

On the wall the massed, awed people of Jericho were as silent as the silent, mysterious, marching army.

And nothing happened. Joshua and the generals completed the circuit of Jericho and led the way back to camp. In the dusk of evening the silent army wound away to the camp, and the priests with their ark and their silent trumpets still marched on behind.

Six days in a row the strange army of Israel came out of camp, and made the silent, ghostly march around the demoralized, mystified town of Jericho. And every day, and every day again, the seven priests with the ark, and the seven priests with the silent black ram's-horn trumpets marched mysteriously on behind the circling army.

Six silent days the army moved around Jericho in ghostly march, yet nothing happened. Now it was the seventh day. On the seventh day the army came out of the camp again in the same way as before, but this day it came much earlier—it was hardly dawn. From the wall of Jericho the marchers could hardly be seen. Only the whispering shuffle of the thousands of distant feet came up to the ears of the watchers on the wall. It was still hardly daylight when the circling army finished the march around Jericho. But now there was a disturbing change. The army did not go back into camp as on all the days before. It silently began marching around the wall a second time.

All that day the watchers on the wall of Jericho stood and kept count. There the Israelites came again in their dreadful silence. Now the army of Israel was beginning the seventh circle of the town. This was the seventh time, but on they came, as silent and as dreadful as before.

Nerves worn raw, tired and stiff from their all-day vigil

on the wall, the demoralized watchers began leaving the wall from sheer unnerved exhaustion. But away from the wall they had no rest either; they rushed back again. Suddenly someone pointed. There was a change—a change at last, something was changing in the circling army. Look! No, look there. Not at Joshua and the generals and the leaders—there at the end of the line of march, at the priests with that oblong box they had circled around Jericho all these days, and seven times this seventh day. Watch them now—something was changing there. No, it wasn't the seven priests with the black box either, it was the seven priests with the seven horns. Look—they were lifting the long black horns to their lips. . . . There was going to be a change, there was going to be a sound at last. The seven priests were going to blow the seven long horns. And there it came—in unison—a long raw blast from the ram's-horn trumpets. The first sound from that silent circling army bounced against the wall of Jericho. It was— it must be a signal. What was going to happen now?

Ah, look there. Look now at the head of the column, at their leader! He had poked his spear high in the air. Now he was waving it for a signal. At the signal of the lifted, swinging spear a great sudden shout roared up from the army of Israel. It was such a cry it seemed to shudder against the wall of Jericho. No, it wasn't the shout, the wall itself was shuddering. The wall was shaking. The wall rocked under the feet of the people. The wall heaved up—the mighty wall was tottering, it was falling!

It couldn't be, but it was falling. The great wall was peel-

ing away from the town, and then it fell the way a hewn tree falls with a great thunderous crashing, with a sound of doom, the sound of the awful end of everything. All the wall—all the wall all around the town on every side. No, not all! As if cut off with a giant knife, one little portion remained standing. And on the portion of standing wall stood the house with the piece of scarlet rope still hanging from its window—the rope not even stirring or whiplashing in the thunderous fall of the whole wall.

There the huge impenetrable, unsurmountable wall lay flat, brought down by a shout and a trumpet blast, and as the wall fell Jericho fell. The Israelite army stormed over the flattened wall into the city. The mop-up, the slaughter began, but the battle was over before it began; Jericho had fallen with its wall. This was the slaughter.

Even before the mop-up of Jericho was over the two spies made their way to Rahab's house where it rose alone on its piece of wall like a lighthouse on a lone rock. But when the spies made their way into the house, they found Rahab's house full—the woman had brought in her father and mother and brothers and sisters, yes, and all her relatives. The house was full of Rahab's red-headed clan. But that had hardly been the agreement—the spies insisted they had only promised to spare Rahab. At last, not knowing what else to do, the puzzled men took Rahab and her whole red-headed household before Joshua. Let Joshua decide!

But there Rahab took over from the spies. She coolly looked up at the great Joshua, and simply said, "It is just this—your spies swore to me that they'd spare me and all that I had. Well, these are mine—never mind my house and furnishings—but these are my people."

Ah, the red-headed woman was as shrewd and cool and bold as she'd been with the Jericho guard. Joshua looked at the spies for confirmation. The two men helplessly shrugged their shoulders. "We may have said it—even sworn it—we could have promised almost anything in the tenseness of that moment, and we were tremendously grateful. But she'd said she lived alone, and we took it to mean when she said all she had she meant all her household furnishings."

There was an interruption. Messengers came for further orders from Joshua. Jericho was completely taken, the captains in the ruined town wanted further instructions. Joshua turned away from Rahab, looked at Jericho. There lay the burning town, flattened and small and despoiled. Jericho, the first stronghold in the conquest of Canaan, had gone down with a shout. Before this first victory—God's victory—Joshua was solemn. "Cursed," he pronounced slowly, "will be the man that builds up Jericho. He shall lay the foundation on his firstborn, and he shall set the gates on his youngest son."

They all looked at Jericho, all but the woman Rahab. There she stood cool and collected, turned to Joshua, outwaiting Joshua, her back turned to the smoldering town.

But Joshua looked at Jericho. "Tell the soldiers," he instructed the messengers, "take salt. Salt Jericho down. Salt it to be a heap and a desolation forever."

Now at last he turned to the woman, Rahab. "Let it be then at your word, woman of Jericho, that what you said the two spies swore to you. You saved the spies. You and your household are now part of the people of Israel."

Then at Joshua's word the army marched away from salted Jericho. And in the midst of the victorious army marched Rahab and her red-headed clan.

THE LEFT HAND OF EHUD

And Joshua said unto all the people, "Thus saith the Lord God of Israel. 'I brought your fathers out of Egypt. . . . And ye went over Jordan and came unto Jericho. . . . And I have given you a land for which ye did not labor, and cities which ye built not, and ye dwell in them. Now therefore fear the Lord, and serve him.' "

And the people said, "The Lord God will we serve."

And the people served the Lord all the days of Joshua, and all the days of the elders that outlived Joshua, who had seen all the great works of the Lord, that he did for Israel.

And that generation were gathered unto their fathers.

And there arose another generation after them, which knew not the Lord, nor yet the works which he had done for Israel. And the children of Israel did evil in the sight of the Lord. And they forsook the Lord God of their fathers, and followed other gods of the people that were round about them.

And the anger of the Lord was hot against Israel, and he delivered them into the hands of their enemies round about.

Nevertheless the Lord raised up judges, which delivered Israel out of the hand of those that spoiled them.

From JOSHUA 24 *and* JUDGES 2

AFTER Joshua and Caleb, the two great generals of the conquest of Canaan, had died, and Israel had taken possession of the conquered land, there came a long period of time when Israel was often leaderless. The heathen countries round about Israel all had their kings. In those countries, son succeeded father to the throne, king succeeded king, but Israel as yet had no king. No king, and no ruling house.

From time to time strong men arose in Israel and led the Israelites in battle against the surrounding heathen nations, but when the strong man died, his son did not succeed him, and Israel would again be leaderless. These strong men that led Israel in battle, and sort of ruled over the affairs of the people of Israel, were called judges. When a judge died there often was no one immediately to take his place, and Israel waited helpless and leaderless—sometimes for years—for another strong man to arise out of their midst and lead them in battle and rule over them.

In the leaderless periods when there was no judge, the surrounding heathen countries took full advantage of Israel's helplessness. They marched in with their armies, conquered the leaderless tribes, and enslaved and oppressed them. Until in Israel some man arose strong enough to throw off the yoke of oppression and slavery. The land would have peace while he lived. Thus in the period of the judges, Israel seesawed back and forth between freedom and slavery, strength and helplessness.

The first such judge was Othniel—he was the son of Caleb's younger brother. Othniel judged Israel and led Israel in battle for forty years. But Othniel died, and there was no one to take his place.

Soon after Othniel's death, Eglon, the heathen king of the neighboring country of Moab, came with his Moabite armies to do battle with the leaderless tribes. The helpless tribes went down before Eglon, and Eglon took possession of the land of Israel.

For eighteen years the tribes of Israel were slaves to Eglon, King of Moab. And every year of the eighteen years the burden of Eglon grew heavier. Every year the fat, pig-greedy Eglon demanded more from the poor, crushed tribes. He took and took, and they gave and gave, but Eglon took so much that every year there was less to give—still Eglon always demanded more.

Now in the nineteenth year of their subjection the time of the year had come again to bring the yearly tribute to Eglon, King of Moab. But after eighteen years of his greedy tyranny there was so little left. The Israelites managed to gather a bit of gold, a handful of silver, a skinny, mangy drove of goats and sheep, and a few poor cows—the best and fattest they could find in the land. Then they looked at what they had gathered. It was worth a man's life to deliver such a ragged tribute to the moody, fat tyrant, Eglon. Last year Eglon had become so enraged with the poor tribute, none of the party sent to bring it to him had come back alive. And this year it was worse, and it was less. Every year everything got a little worse, a little hungrier, and more desperate and more hopeless. . . .

Eglon was a despot and a tyrant. He'd grown fat off the poor tribes of Israel that he held completely in his power. He'd grown so fat that his eyes were sunk in his head—he could hardly look out of his little, pig-greedy eyes in his puffed, many-chinned face—but the little pig eyes could still see that always the tribute was poor and not enough. Never enough! Now who this year was to bring this poorest of all tributes to Eglon? Last year none had come back.

The tribes held secret counsel. Perhaps they shouldn't waste good men on it again this year. Perhaps make up a tribute party of expendable men. Men who wouldn't be worth much as fighters and battlers if it ever came to the time of utter desperation when the tribes would have to rebel and rise up against Eglon. But that small hope lay in the hapless future. The time was now—the tribute had to be paid and delivered now—the day of tribute was drawing near.

Well, why not Ehud, then? The left-handed Ehud of the tribe of Benjamin? A left-handed man certainly wasn't much good in war or battle. Awkward and clumsy, when a left-handed man pulled out his sword with his left hand, he was as likely to stick and slash his neighbor in the ranks as an enemy—more likely. Left-handedness did not become a soldier. Send Ehud then, who was left-handed, left-handed in everything. Send the left-handed Ehud at the head of a left-handed band to deliver the tribute. Save the good men for the rebellion which would have to come. The idea had all-around appeal—send Ehud.

Ehud, the Benjaminite, knew exactly why he had been chosen from among the twelve tribes. It wasn't any honor, it was a sentence. It might even be a death sentence. But Ehud was not surprised, nor particularly bitter. He was used to it —from childhood on he had been teased and jeered at for his total left-handedness—he even ate left-handed! And when, in childhood games with other boys, he threw a spear or drew a wooden sword, the others had always yelled out, "Watch it. Ehud's going to throw." Then they'd all scatter in so-called terror of his aimless left-handed clumsiness. They'd never admit he could toss a wooden spear as well and as far and as accurately as the next one. Left-handedness became a joke that had followed Ehud all his life, even as a grown man. Now it had caught up with him, and the joke was done—this meant almost certain death.

In silence Ehud accepted the assignment that the delegation from the tribes had come to bring to him. It was a short assignment. There wasn't much to say when a man was being assigned to almost certain doom. The leader of the delegation was brief. "Ehud, you are the man, and tomorrow is the day. We've brought you a small party of other left-handed men to help you deliver the tribute to Eglon. Don't fail us. If you don't deliver the tribute tomorrow, Eglon will send his soldiers to rob and plunder and kill."

Ehud didn't answer, but looked beyond the delegation at the little group of left-handed men. Over the heads of the delegation he spoke only one sentence to the left-handed men. "Be at my door tomorrow morning well before dawn."

Without another look at the delegation, he turned and went into the house, closed the door. He'd show them what could be accomplished by a left-handed man, but why waste time in talk—there were things to be done. He'd show them.

From under a secret board in the floor in his one-room

mountain hut Ehud dug out a tightly wrapped trumpet and a long piece of an old broken sword. He'd show them.

Late into the night, with the whole village sleeping, Ehud worked on the two-foot-long piece of sword that he had treasured and hidden so long. He had nothing but a broken piece of grindstone with which to work on the sword. He ground and rubbed down the old blade until it was as thin and pliable and savage as a razor. But unlike a razor he gave it two edges, and he honed both edges to a vicious, paper-thin sharpness. Only where his hand had to hold the sword blade did he round the edges so as not to cut his hand too much.

Again and again Ehud reached under his robes and fitted the flat thin blade against his bare body. It had to lie flat and smooth, it had to follow the shape of his thigh and the curve of his leg. Then—impatient with fumbling with his robe—he took off his robe altogether, and ground and honed again until the blade was so pliable that it followed the movement of his leg as, naked, he strode up and down the barred, shuttered room of his cabin.

At last Ehud was satisfied. With a flat leather thong he tied the sword to his waist, then with a flat narrow strap he fastened the tip of the point to his leg. He put on his robe. Now he practiced drawing the long dagger until he could smoothly and swiftly pull it out through a small slit in the fold of his robe, without cutting himself or ripping and widening the tiny slit. All his practice with the piece of sword blade had been done with the left hand. Now Ehud took up the old trumpet and practiced handling the trumpet with his right hand. He practiced until picking it up and laying it down with the right hand almost felt natural to him. He could only hope that it looked as natural as it was beginning to feel.

When Ehud finished practicing, it was morning. The day for delivering the tribute to Eglon, King of Moab, had come. It was still dark, but now it was time to set out with his party of left-handed men, gather the tribute, and take it down the mountains to Eglon.

When Ehud opened his barred door the doomed party of left-handed men was silently waiting outside. Ehud gave the men few instructions.

All he really needed them for was to carry the booty, lead the little drove of goats and sheep, and help the skinny cows down the mountain paths. "When we get there, act properly humble, but keep your mouths shut," he instructed. "Let me do all the talking. And no weapons! You can be sure we'll be searched before they let us go in to the king, and if they find as much as a small stone on any of us . . ." He made a significant sound and drew his hand across his throat.

Ehud left nothing to chance. He personally searched all his men, ran his hands down their sides, paying particular attention to their right side—the side from which a left-handed man would have to pull a concealed weapon. When he had searched them all, he lifted his trumpet high and ordered the man nearest him to search him.

The man did not hesitate—too much was at stake. He thoroughly patted Ehud all over, rubbed his hands hard along Ehud's right side, pursed his lips, went over Ehud's right side once more. "Put that hand with the trumpet down," he ordered. "Raising your arm pulls your robe away from your body."

Ehud obeyed. The man poked and patted again. At last he looked up. "Nothing," he said glumly.

Ehud grinned at him. "Now shall we start?"

The man nodded somberly.

Without fanfare, without awakening the sleeping village, the left-handed party started down the mountainside to bring the tribute of the tribes to Eglon. Ehud led the way, carrying only the trumpet. Strangely, no one remarked on the trumpet; the men were in no mood to ask questions. But as the day dawned one of the men suddenly remarked, "That's odd—you carrying that trumpet in your right hand!"

Ehud stopped suddenly. "Why? Doesn't it look natural? Don't I handle it right? I practiced all night."

The man pulled his face into a wry smile. "Seems a long time to wait to learn to become right-handed—your last night on earth."

Ehud laughed. They marched on again.

They reached the palace of Eglon in the heat of the day. It was early afternoon, and in the hot valley below the mountains the air was stifling, not a breeze stirred and a brassy sun bore down. Ehud and his men were promptly and thoroughly searched by a captain of the guard and three soldiers. But it was too stifling hot for the soldiers to bestir themselves and be entirely thorough. The Israelites were searched, but they were not stripped. Ehud drew a deep breath—it was going as he had planned. That was why he had started down the mountains in dawn darkness to be at the gates of the palace in the hottest part of the day.

Now the guard opened the gate to the courtyard of the palace, and again the heat worked in Ehud's favor. The guard ordered them to leave the drove of goats and sheep and the fifteen poor cows in the courtyard. At least King Eglon would not see the half-starved beasts immediately. But it was even better than that—Eglon it seemed was not in the main palace. Because of the heat the fat king had retired to his summer parlor—a latticed structure in the shaded end of the cucumber garden behind the main palace. Now a chamberlain came from the summer parlor to lead Ehud and his party to the king.

But Ehud turned to the captain of the guard. "These men were merely sent along to help deliver the tribute, but I was given a secret message to deliver in person to the king." He tapped the trumpet in his right hand significantly. "This trumpet is the Israelite sign that I carry a message. . . . But perhaps the great king in this stifling heat should not be annoyed with all my party—the men are dirty and sweaty, and—well—a bit smelly from struggling down the mountain with goats and cows and sheep."

"All Israelites are smelly," the captain said gruffly. "It doesn't need goats." The chamberlain laughed. Ehud inclined his head humbly. But the captain of the guard nodded to his men, and Ehud's party was marched back to the outer courtyard. Between the captain and the chamberlain Ehud was led into the summer parlor at the far end of the cucumber garden.

King Eglon seemed in an excellent mood, and accepted the gold and the silver and the carved gifts from Ehud's hand. As the king studied the gifts, Ehud covertly studied the summer parlor—the one door. Then to cover up he made respectful mention of the gift of goats and sheep and fifteen cows in the outer courtyard.

"But that is not all, oh, King," Ehud added humbly. "I was given a secret message to deliver only to you. It is so secret that even my men mustn't know of it, so if the king pleases, I would like permission to lead my party back over the border into their own country—that way they can't possibly do any mischief—but I would like to be permitted to come back alone to deliver my secret message." He gestured meaningfully with the trumpet in his right hand. "May I be permitted to leave my trumpet here—as an excuse for me to return without my men? I would suddenly remember I had forgotten my trumpet, and go back alone."

The king had listened all the while he was studying the tribute in gold and in silver, and mentally adding the worth of the gifts, but now he looked curiously from the gifts to the trumpet, and curtly nodded his permission. Ehud respectfully walked backward out of the presence of Eglon's majesty, and backed out of the door of the summer parlor.

Ehud led his left-handed party back into Israel as far as the quarries at Gilgal, and there he called a halt. For the first time his face broke into a smile. "It worked, men. I told Eglon I had to come back alone to deliver a secret message. So now I'm going back alone, and if anything still goes wrong, it's only one, and not our whole party, that doesn't get out alive. Wait for me, and if all goes well and according to plan, you'll hear my trumpet. And when you hear it, come to me at once. But if not—well, wait for me until dark and then go to your homes."

The men looked with new respect at this Ehud, who'd been picked as their leader only because he was even more hopelessly left-handed than they. And Ehud read their thoughts. "Maybe if things work out," he said mysteriously, "we can show what can be done with the left hand."

"We'll wait for you—we'll wait until dawn, Ehud," one of the men said.

Once more, between chamberlain and captain, Ehud was led into the summer parlor in the cucumber garden. King Eglon was waiting for him. In fact, because of the importance he attached to the secret message, he sat in state in the throne chair at one end of the summer parlor.

As Ehud marched directly before the throne his heart sank. The room was filled with servants and guards and retainers—he'd overplayed his hand—behind the king's chair even stood a row of important-looking military officers. But as a man bold with an enormous, important secret, Ehud loudly and boldly announced, "I have a message not only from the tribes of Israel, but from the God of Israel for you, oh, King." And, though he stood before the king, Ehud dared to turn away to look significantly at all the servants and guards and retainers in the room.

The king's shrewd little eyes followed Ehud's roving look. Then, the little pig eyes almost shut, the king said in fat, oily tones, "This Israelite seems to trust no one."

And Ehud answered simply, "I did not trust the men of my own party. Who can one trust in these days, oh, King?"

The statement appealed to the suspicious-minded king. He studied Ehud. Then he made up his mind, clapped his hands, and ordered, "Everybody out."

While the men were filing out of the room, Ehud picked up the trumpet and carried it over and laid it on the single step before the throne chair and the king. And the two waited in silence before each other until the last man had left and the door of the summer parlor had clicked shut. Ehud stirred at the trumpet with his toe like a man who has such an important message he doesn't know how to begin or how to frame the words. And the king bent his fat body and looked at the trumpet before his feet. "Is the message in the trumpet?" he demanded curiously.

Ehud said nothing, picked up the trumpet with his right hand, and raised it slowly. The fat king peered into the horn of the trumpet as if expecting to see a message hidden there. Ehud raised the trumpet still higher, and the king stood up.

As the king arose, Ehud's left hand snaked toward his side. For a silent swift moment the shining dagger made from a sword glimmered, the next moment the dagger, handle and all, plunged into the huge, fat king. With a sighing gasp, like

a great sack of softness, the big king fell forward on the dagger and lay still at Ehud's feet. It was very still in the shaded summer parlor behind the lattices—cool and still.

Without bothering about the dagger on which he had worked so hard and long, Ehud stepped over the king and went to the door. He did not hurry or panic, and at the door of the summer parlor he waited and listened long. At last he slipped out of the door, shut and locked it behind him. Slowly, thoughtfully, Ehud walked across the outer courtyard to the sentries at the gate. One of the sentries opened the gate. Quietly, and with only a muttered thank you to the captain of the guard, Ehud walked through the gate—a man deep in thought. Then he turned as if suddenly remembering something important, and coolly he said to the captain of the guard, "I almost forgot. But I delivered my message to the king, and he is pondering it and does not want to be disturbed by anyone. He ordered me to tell you. And I believe he talked of taking a nap afterward."

"If the king ordered it," the captain said stiffly, "the king's orders will be obeyed."

"I should hope so," Ehud said innocently. "It was quite a message I gave your king."

He walked off unhurriedly—again seemingly lost in thought—until he was lost from sight. Then Ehud hurried. But it wasn't until he was nearing the quarries at Gilgal, where his men must be waiting, that Ehud felt safe enough to raise the trumpet to his lips and blow a mighty blast.

The blast that Ehud blew seemed to fall into the quarries

of Gilgal, swirl and multiply around the deep rock walls, then leap out to go crashing through the mountains. It was such a victory blast as had not been heard in the land of Israel in eighteen years.

The party of left-handed men rushed out to Ehud. But Ehud still went on blowing his trumpet, blew it until his lip split. Between breaths he told his men of his triumph over Eglon, the gross, fat tyrant, Eglon. And over the quarries of Gilgal he blew the marching notes of the armies of Israel. When Ehud could blow no more, the little band passed the trumpet from hand to hand and still blew on. Blew the alert. The trumpet sounds went leaping through the mountains.

At last—faintly—from other mountains the sounds came echoing back. The people had heard and recognized the triumphant marching call of Ehud's summoning trumpet.

From under the floors of huts and cabins the people must have brought out trumpets as old as the trumpets of Jericho —trumpets still left from the conquering armies of Canaan that had been handed down from father to son. The alert of summoning trumpets ran through the mountains from cabin to cabin and village to village, and it reached the towns. From everywhere over the mountains the people came rushing to Ehud at the quarries of Gilgal. They came with the weapons they had, came with rusted spears and broken swords, and ancient bows and arrows—hidden against the coming of this great day. They came with ox yokes and the thick, stout handles of farming tools; they came with whatever had lain at hand.

Ehud took the leadership of the mob that poured down the

mountains to join him. With his motley, crazily weaponed followers he rushed down the mountain from Gilgal back to the palace of Eglon. He waved his battered trumpet high. "On to the palace of Eglon!"

Even as far as the palace of Eglon, they had heard the faint trumpets sounding everywhere in the mountains of Israel. They became uneasily aware of a stirring in the mountains. They expected no rebellion from the slave people of Israel to whom they'd left no weapons and in whom they'd left no will to fight. But a messenger, escaped from the first outpost attacked by Ehud, rushed startling news to the palace.

At the palace the guards and the king's chamberlain, greatly disturbed, summoned the king's army officers, but they, too, stood undecided. They agreed that King Eglon must be notified of a possible uprising, but the king still slept in the summer parlor in the cucumber garden, and it was worth a man's life to wake up the moody tyrant when he'd locked himself in for a long nap in his cool retreat. Night was falling, and with the falling of night the trumpets in the hills and mountains of Israel seemed also to have fallen silent —perhaps the brief, weaponless uprising had been quelled. Perhaps it was best to wait for a further message, and not disturb King Eglon with the news of a flurry at one insignificant mountain outpost.

A new message came, a grave warning that there was a general uprising in the mountains, a great shadowy movement of a mass of people coming down from the mountains at Gilgal in the night. The rebellion was spreading, other outposts had fallen, an army, or a mob, was moving to take the fords of the River Jordan. Now there was no choice for the king's chamberlain and the army officers—Eglon had to be told the news. Still they hesitated; they knew the tyrant too well. But the king's chamberlain suddenly thought back—they had only the word of the Israelite with the trumpet that King Eglon was not to be disturbed. And that was hours ago—in all those hours King Eglon had not called for food or drink. But wasn't that unnatural? Wasn't that all wrong?

Eglon's going without food for hours decided them. They rushed to the summer parlor.

The chamberlain tried the door, whispered to the officers. Now the officers shouted orders to their men. The men rammed the locked door until at last it flew open. There lay Eglon, there lay their king, like a lumpish hippopotamus, gross and fat and dead. He lay on his face with a dagger sunk into him—even the handle.

The officers and men and the king's chamberlain were still standing around the body of their king when the Israelite mob came storming through the cucumber garden. At their head came Ehud, a great Moabite sword in his left hand.

It was too late for anything. Too late to escape, too late to defend the summer parlor. Ehud seemed everywhere, Ehud and his great sword. Cool and accomplished and skillful, he guided his mob in the slaughter. Again death came into the cucumber garden as the officers and leaders of the armies of Moab went down around their dead king. Now it was Moab that was leaderless. But Israel had Ehud. And before Ehud and his mighty left hand all Moab went down in defeat.

THE STARS IN THEIR COURSES

The song of Deborah and Barak, the son of Abinoam, on
that day:

In the days of Jael, the highways were unoccupied,
And the travelers walked through byways.
The inhabitants of the villages ceased,
They ceased in Israel.
Was there a shield or spear seen
Among forty thousand in Israel?

Awake, awake, Deborah.
Arise, Barak, thou son of Abinoam.

Praise ye the Lord for the avenging of Israel,
When the people willingly offered themselves.
The stars in their courses fought against Sisera.
The river of Kishon swept them away,
The ancient river, the River Kishon.
Then were the horsehoofs broken
By the means of the prancings,
The prancings of their mighty ones.

So let all thine enemies perish, O Lord.

Arranged from JUDGES 6

EIGHTY years the land had rest under the leadership of the left-handed Ehud, and even after Ehud died there was sweet peace and a surcease from the struggle and strife with the surrounding heathen kingdoms. Oh, the Philistines had dared to come up against Israel, but the mighty Shamgar, son of Anath, took care of that singlehanded. With nothing in that single hand but an ox goad, Shamgar smote six hundred Philistines. And again there was peace.

Now, however, peace was just a memory. Things had come to such a pass in the last twenty years that no man dared to stand up after Shamgar, and be a judge in Israel. Stand up? Rise up? The men of Israel did not even dare to move upright along the roads and highways of their own country. They skulked about by side roads and byways, and by hidden tracks and footpaths in the mountains. The villages were half empty—men dwelt in holes and caves of the mountains.

A man stand up against the Canaanites? It was worth a man's life to go down a road in daylight. The terror of Sisera and his nine hundred chariots of iron was in all the highways of the land.

Nine hundred chariots of iron! The whole might of Jabin, King of the Canaanites, lay in those chariots, and Sisera was his general. Who could stand up against Sisera and his iron chariots? The man hadn't lost a battle in twenty years!

The iron chariots patrolled the roads and the highways of Israel, conscripting the slave men of Israel for the Canaanite armies of King Jabin. And if a man resisted, the horses rode him down, the iron chariot crushed him.

The chariots went everywhere to conscript and to confiscate. The charioteers searched the country and all the villages and towns along the highways. They conscripted the men, they confiscated the weapons of war to prevent any rebellion from as much as beginning. When the charioteers found no men and no weapons, they took the boys and the girls—any likely-looking lad, any pretty young woman. They took them back to their own country for their own pleasure, they took them into slavery in Canaan.

Few ever returned to Israel. There was Barak, son of Abinoam, one of the few fortunate ones. He, too, had been taken away as a lad, he'd been pressed into the service of Sisera, as the keeper of Sisera's horses and of Sisera's own iron chariot. For years he had been gone, now he'd come back a grown man—a big man. But now that he was back, he hid in the mountains of Kedesh-Naphtali. What else could the man do? His spirit had been broken, like that of the other men of Israel, but he had more reason—he had been a slave to Sisera's horses. He seethed with hatred for Sisera, but he hid in a cave.

In the cave in the mountains of Ephraim, other dispossessed men gathered with Barak. They plotted revenge, but what were a few empty-handed men to do against iron chariots? From his hiding place Barak sent out his hopeless, desperate gang of cave dwellers to feel out the countryside, test the feelings of the people—see if they were ready for rebellion against King Jabin of Canaan, and Sisera and his nine hundred chariots of iron. The men found only abject terror. At best, men were willing to fight if they had weapons—hopeless as it was for a man with a spear or a sword to come up against a chariot of iron. But they'd fight if they had a spear or a sword. They hadn't any.

Barak plotted and schemed in his cave, began gathering a few weapons, but could do little more. What could a man do? After twenty years of Jabin and Sisera things had come to such a pass that there wasn't even a man as judge over Israel. No man dared to rise up as a leader. Israel had a woman as judge—Deborah. She was really a prophetess and a poetess, but she also judged the people. For lack of a man and a leader, the people went to her to settle their quarrels and petty problems.

Deborah sat in white robes under the palm tree of Deborah and gave out judgment to the people that came to her. The Canaanites allowed it. They tolerated Deborah. She was a woman—wrote poetry and prophesied wild things. It seemed safe enough. A woman could not lead Israel into battle, a woman wasn't likely to stir up rebellion. It seemed harmless. Keep the Israelites poor and scared and weaponless, but let them have this woman in white robes to run to—it kept the slave people more satisfied.

But Deborah secretly summoned Barak, the renegade slave, to come to her under the palm tree of Deborah. Somehow the woman knew he was in hiding in Kedesh-Naphtali. Barak obediently left his hideout, and went to her.

Now Barak stood before the woman in white. Her black eyes flashed as she looked up at the big young man. She stood up. "The Lord God of Israel has commanded—go to Mount Tabor, and take with you ten thousand men. And God will draw Sisera to the River Kishon—Sisera with his chariots and his multitude. And God will deliver him into your hand."

Barak looked at her dumbfounded. "Ten thousand men? Are you mad? Well, yes, I can round up ten thousand men. I can maybe round up forty thousand. But there aren't enough spears and swords and shields. . . . Let's say we could get together enough old rusty weapons to arm ten thousand men —what then? What are ten thousand poorly armed men against nine hundred chariots and charioteers, and all of Sisera's foot soldiers besides?"

"The stars in their courses will fight with you, Barak," Deborah said mysteriously.

Barak shrugged. "Believe me, I've worked on this for months. My men have felt out the tribes. Well, we can count on a few fighting men from the tribes of Benjamin and Issachar and Ephraim, but mostly they all have to come from Zebulun and Naphtali. Those are the only two tribes that really seem to have the will to fight—because they're the most desperate, they've taken about all from Sisera and the Canaanites that a man's able to take and still stay a man."

"And you, Barak? Have you the will to fight and lead them?" Deborah demanded.

The big man, broken in slavery—having only his hate— did not quite look up at the woman in white. "Shall we put it this way? If you go, I will go. But if not, I won't take it on myself to lead ten thousand hopeless men to their destruction." He clenched his hands. "Oh, but if I could only get my hands—my two hands—on Sisera!"

The prophetess looked at Barak's big, strong hands. "I will go with you," she said quietly. "But never mind your hands, Barak, for now hear the words of the Lord—because you need a woman to lead you against Sisera, the victory shall also go to a woman. Sisera shall not fall into your hands —Sisera shall die by the hands of a woman."

Openly Deborah, the prophetess in white, journeyed with Barak into the heights of Mount Tabor. Openly she and Barak gathered the weapons and ten thousand men for the rebellion against King Jabin and Sisera. They did not hide their movements. Boldly in the daytime, day after day, they gathered on the ridges and peaks of lower Tabor. It was by Deborah's command. Barak had counseled secrecy and hiding, but Deborah overruled Barak. Deborah seemed in command.

It worked as the prophetess had planned. The movements and gathering of the rebels were reported to Sisera, and drew Sisera and his hosts and his iron chariots to Mount Tabor. . . .There came the nine hundred chariots rolling at the head of the army of Canaanites into the valley of the River Kishon. The valley was bone dry, the river was low, the nine hundred chariots rolled on through the river, on into the valley, on toward the foothills of Tabor.

The iron chariots plowed on through the deep sand of the dry river valley, but the crowd of hastily organized, poorly armed Israelites did not come down from the mountain. They stood out against the steep sides of the mountain like ants crawling along the sides of their anthill, but they didn't come down. The chariots in the river valley could not go up into the mountains. Night was falling. Sisera called a halt in the valley of the Kishon. The Canaanites camped.

Up in the mountain the Israelites waited. For Deborah, the prophetess, had foretold that the Lord God of Israel was coming to do battle for his people. God came in the night. In the night the rains came, a great deluge of outpouring rain. The water gushed and swirled and roared down the mountain. The rain roared.

In the morning, when Sisera arose and looked out of his tent, the water still washed down the mountains. The Israelites clung like wet rats to the sides of the gushing mountain. The watery rocks must be as slippery as melting ice. The poor wretches clung to the mountain to keep from being washed down.

Sisera looked behind him. The Kishon River seemed to rise up at him. The river was swollen and enormous. The river roared. And then the river raged over its banks, the water raced over the plain. The water from the mountains raced down to the plain to meet the floodwaters of the river.

The nine hundred chariots—even Sisera's own chariot—were mired in the sand and the silt and the swirling water. Still the rain came down and still the river roared up, the water washed up against the chariot wheels. The rain came down all that day, and the day began drawing toward evening.

In the evening's half darkness the Israelites began coming down from Mount Tabor, came slipping, came sliding, came like a dark flowing current more ominous and dark than the water coming down. They came on with their shields held over their heads, spilling water. They came on with their wet spears. The Israelites kept coming. But the rain stopped.

Now that the rain had at last stopped, Sisera ordered the chariots up out of the valley, up toward the mountain. He studied the mountainside. To Sisera's astonishment a woman in white seemed to be leading the Israelites. She stood out

white against the black, wet mountain. She was singing! Came on in her white robe singing a wild song to men that came lunging after her. Beside her plunged a big man without a shield or a helmet, but swinging a great sword over his head as if in time to the white woman's song. . . . But wasn't that Barak, his renegade slave, his own personal slave?

With wild curses Sisera ordered the chariots ahead. "Ride them down, crush them under the wheels, but get me the woman in white and the renegade slave!"

At Sisera's orders the men whiplashed the horses. The horses staggered up, the horses lunged, but they broke their hoofs, smashed their heels against the immovable chariots. The horses screamed and staggered up again under the slashing whips of the charioteers, but the chariots would not stir. And if one did break loose and lunge ahead, it only crashed into the chariot ahead. The valley of the Kishon became a madness of struggling, crazed men, clanging iron, and screaming horses.

The desperate Sisera, the man who had never lost a battle, saw clearly the hopelessness of the mad struggle, and suddenly he ran. He left his men to the battle and the struggle, but he jumped off his mired chariot, and ran off on foot in the gathering darkness. Hood drawn over his bronze helmet and down over his face—as if against the rain, but so that no one would recognize him as the general—Sisera made his way on foot among the tangled chariots. The great Sisera was deserting his men—on foot.

The Israelites slaughtered Sisera's men. They showed the

marauding, looting charioteers no mercy; no quarter was given. The most merciful thing they did was to let the few chariots that broke loose from the mire plunge into the swollen river. The iron chariots pulled the horses under, the river swept the men away.

Now Barak's army turned on the hapless, disorganized foot soldiers, forced them back toward the roaring river. But Barak left his men to the mop-up. He and his party of hastily appointed officers searched among the mired, empty chariots for Sisera. They had missed Sisera. They searched frantically —night was falling. The battle was won, but to make it a total victory they needed Sisera. If he got away, he could organize another army and come back again.

The search party spread out from the chariots. If the river had not gotten Sisera, he had run away. But he wouldn't run far in his heavy armor in the heavy wet sand. They had no armor to hamper them. "Spread out," Barak ordered. "Get Sisera! Get him alive and bring him to me." He had tossed away his great sword; he held up his two big hands.

Alone in the night Sisera slogged on. If only the low-hanging rain clouds would lift, but the clouds came down from the mountains, and slid down the foothills, and filled the valley. It was difficult to see, impossible to tell directions.

For a while Sisera still had the roar of the river and the clang and the shouts and screams of battle to guide him out of the valley. But the clouds pressed down and the darkness. It became impossible to tell whether he was making headway or slogging in weary circles in the miry valley.

The man's gasping breath rasped out in the stillness and darkness. Once more he wearily stopped, shed another part of his heavy armor. He took pains to stamp it down into the soggy sand and scuff dirt over it. Otherwise he would be leaving a sure trail—the wrought armor of a general. He'd kept it on too long, now he could hardly lift one weary foot before the other. But the hunt for him must be on—he was sure of it. Now that they had captured the mired chariots, he was the prize—the biggest prize.

If only the clouds would lift and a few stars come out—just a few. He needed something by which to set a course. He made himself believe that he was finally getting up out of the valley, his feet did not seem to sink down quite so far in the mire. But if he was now going up toward the foothills, then he would be in really treacherous country, and he must be extra careful. Here somewhere must be the borders of Israel and Canaan, but here too somewhere must be the borders of the Kenites. The Kenites were at peace with the Canaanites—they would have to give him sanctuary. But where was their border, and which was the border of Israel? If in the darkness and in his blind weariness he stumbled into Israel, then all his running and weary slogging would have been for nothing. He had never shown those Israelites one grain of mercy, he could expect none. There was only one mercy—if the stars came out, he could set a course toward the border of the Kenites.

He shed the last of his armor, and now he had nothing left but the bronze helmet with the insignia of his generalship. In his weariness it was far too heavy to wear, but he still carried it in his hand—reluctant to let go of this last sign that he was Sisera, captain of the hosts of Jabin, King of the Canaanites. He tried to bury the remainder of his princely armor, but he found only a thin layer of silt covering rock. All he could do was to scrape up the dirt and heap it over the armor. But it gave him new heart—rock—he had blundered his way into the foothills.

Was he imagining it? Was he above the cloud layer that had settled down in the valley? Were those stars flickering dimly there out above the foothills? And there—all by itself—was that a big clear star, or was it lamplight?

Ah, now he had hope. He had seen the stars. Now he could set his course by that single clear star in relation to those farther flickering stars above the foothills. Now he had his bearings, now by going toward the star he should be going into the land of the Kenites.

Weary and shivering, Sisera forced himself on. But strange—the big star blotted out, appeared again, blotted out. Now its light stood steady and still above the hills as before. The spent man stopped to study it, tried to fix his gaze, keep his heavy eyes on it. . . . It . . . it wasn't a star! It was the lighted doorway of a herdsman's tent, directly before him on top of the hill. The reason the light had shifted and blotted out and appeared again—somebody was standing in the doorway watching him. Watching him come, waiting for him. He couldn't run—it would be no use. He could do nothing now but to walk on to the tent, hoping it was the tent of a Kenite herdsman.

Now the lit doorway stood out steady and clear. Whoever

had been standing there had left the doorway, had moved out, was coming toward him. Sisera's hand clenched around the strap of his helmet—the only weapon he had left—swung the heavy helmet.

He stood his ground, waited. Let them come. If they came within reach of the helmet . . . He peered into the darkness. It was a woman! A woman alone—the men must be out in the hills herding the flocks. She came straight toward him.

Sisera set the helmet on his head, and as she came near he called out in a commanding, rasping voice, "I am Sisera, captain of the hosts of the Canaanites. . . . Don't be afraid."

The woman answered immediately. "Come into my tent, my lord."

Sisera's knees buckled under him in his relief—the woman had spoken the language of the Kenites.

"Ah," he said. "You are a Kenite—we Canaanites and Kenites are at peace."

"Come in. Come into the tent," she said again. But this time she said what he had said: "Don't be afraid."

It wasn't until he stood in the tent that Sisera realized how thirsty he was. Thirsty in all the soaked wateriness—but standing there helplessly swinging the helmet, waiting for whatever was coming at him, his mouth had gone dry with fear.

And now in his relief at being in the safety of the tent, Sisera's legs began to shake under him. The woman noticed it. She ordered him to lie down. She covered him with her own mantle.

Under the mantle, teeth chattering, Sisera begged her for

a little water. She brought him milk, came with a leather bottle of milk. Ah, milk—he was safe with her. She was no doubt properly cowed and impressed—a meek, simple herdsman's wife before a general. "What did you say your name was?" Sisera asked her.

"I am Jael," she said simply. "Wife of Heber the Kenite."

"Well, Jael," Sisera ordered as he drank the milk, "stand in the doorway of your tent again, just as you were when I came—that makes it look as if you've nothing to hide. But if any men come looking for me, and ask if you've seen anything this night, tell them you've seen nothing."

She nodded and went to the door of the tent. Sisera's eyes almost started to fall shut as he watched her go. He lay back, pulled the mantle over him, and settled down in a dead sleep of exhaustion.

The woman in the doorway was quiet. For a while she remained there as she had been ordered. But the stillness of the man under the mantle changed to a heavy, steady breathing. The woman left the doorway, went around to the back of the tent. When she returned out of the darkness she carried a hammer and a muddy tent pin she had pulled up out of the rain-soaked ground. With the hammer and the tent pin she kneeled down beside Sisera.

Later there were voices, movements in the darkness of the lower hills out toward the valley. The woman opened the door of the quiet tent, stood in the lighted doorway again. She listened. There were voices suddenly close by. Someone must have stumbled on part of the armor over which Sisera had heaped the handfuls of dirt. His excitement made the man forget caution. He yelled out in the night, "Barak, Barak —here's part of his armor—he's been here."

From the doorway the woman saw the men cluster around the spot down the hill where the armor had been found. She went back into her tent, came out with Sisera's helmet. She quietly walked toward the group of excited men studying the spot. Suddenly they became aware of her—they stood up, looked at her, looked at the helmet. She singled out the big man. "Are you Barak? I am Jael, wife of Heber the Kenite. Come with me, and I will show you the man you are looking for."

She led Barak to the tent. She pulled back the mantle. There before Barak's feet lay the great terror, the iron warrior, Sisera, dead—a wooden tent pin driven through his temple. And Barak looked from Sisera to the quiet, composed woman, and Barak remembered the words of Deborah, the prophetess, that because of his lack of faith and courage, the real victory would go to a woman.

Barak stood quiet, and found little to say, except to tell Jael, "You've won the victory. You've made it complete."

And it was almost morning.

Barak and his party left the tent. Weary as they were, they set out immediately to bring the news to Deborah, as if she hadn't foretold it, as if the prophetess didn't already know. As if the poetess, sitting in the tent of Sisera at the site of the battle, had not already penned a battle hymn and a great song of victory in the valley where the River Kishon roared. She recited it to Barak, she taught it to Barak, and the two in the early morning mounted to the chariot of Sisera, and Barak and Deborah sang the song of victory, the song of Deborah, to the victorious ten thousand of Israel. At the end of the song the victory roar of the ten thousand drowned out the roar of the River Kishon and seemed to mount to the heights of Mount Tabor. But it also reached far beyond the valley to where a woman stood listening in the doorway of a lone herdsman's tent in the foothills.

THE BATTLE IS THE LORD'S

And the children of Israel did evil in the sight of the Lord: and the Lord delivered them into the hand of Midian seven years. And the hand of Midian prevailed against Israel: and because of the Midianites the children of Israel made them the dens which are in the mountains, and caves, and strongholds. And so it was, when Israel had sown, that the Midianites came up, and encamped against them, and destroyed the increase of the earth, and left no sustenance for Israel, neither sheep, nor ox, nor ass. For they came up with their cattle and their tents, and they came as grasshoppers for multitude; for both they and their camels were without number. And they entered into the land to destroy it.

And there came an angel of the Lord, and sat under an oak which was in Ophrah. . . . And Gideon threshed wheat by the winepress, to hide it from the Midianites. And the angel of the Lord appeared unto him, and said unto him, "The Lord is with thee, thou mighty man of valor."

And Gideon said unto him, "Oh, my Lord, if the Lord be with us, why then is all this befallen us? But now the Lord hath forsaken us, and delivered us into the hands of the Midianites."

And the Lord looked upon him, and said, "Go in this thy might, and thou shalt save Israel from the hand of the Midianites: have not I sent thee?"

From JUDGES 6

GIDEON was threshing wheat in the winepress. It was no place to thresh wheat, but the sunken winepress hewn deep into the solid rock of the mountainside muffled the steady clop-clop of Gideon's beating flail, and held it within its rock walls. At least, Gideon hoped it did. This harvest time the Midianites were again encamped in the valley below the mountains. Every year these wild nomads of the wilderness came up at harvest time. They didn't raise as much as a wheat stalk themselves; they waited for Israel and harvest time. In the time of harvest they came up with their camels and their tents, and camped below the mountains of Israel until the grain was ripe and the threshing had been done. Then they simply moved in to gather up the grain and cattle for another year. Enslaved Israel worked, the Midianites gathered.

Gideon beat away at the tough grain—it had been harvested too early, and it was still too green for threshing, but if he waited, the Midianites would come and take it. It would have been better to use an ox or bullock to tread out the grain—that was soundless—but the oxen and bullocks, the few that were left from last year's Midianite raid, had already been put into hiding in dens and caves of the mountains. Now if Gideon could still thresh out some early wheat by hand, there might be enough for the hidden animals—if the Midianites didn't find them.

Gideon glanced down the mountain at the distant level valley where the tents of the Midianites stretched row on row. Maybe the Midianites heard the clop-clop of his threshing, maybe it didn't matter to them—they'd come and get it in their good time.

Gideon wiped his forehead and looked up the road. There sat a stranger under the oak beside the house! A Midianite?

A scout sent out ahead? But the wayfarer was different from the Midianites—a strange dress. And he sat there so easily, so self-possessed. Gideon walked toward the wayfaring stranger.

The man looked up. "Hail, mighty man. Hail to you, you mighty man of valor."

Gideon stared in surprise. "Me? You mean me?" Then he snickered. "Mighty man of valor—trying to sneak a bushel of half-ripe wheat before the Midianites can grab it." But Gideon was relieved. If the wayfarer under the oak talked strangely, he at least seemed friendly.

"Yes, you," the stranger said seriously. "The Lord is with you—you mighty man. You are going to save Israel from the Midianites."

More at ease now, Gideon laughed right out. "You're not talking about me! My father's house is the least in the tribe of Manasseh, and I am the least in my father's house—the least and the last, the Midianites butchered all my brothers at Tabor, I'm the only one left. I and my old father, and my young son—and that's the whole house of Gideon . . . So if the Lord is with me," he added bitterly, "then why have we fallen into the hands of the Midianites?"

Gideon, hearing his own bitter words, hastily bethought himself—better not speak out too recklessly, the stranger might not be a Midianite, but he could be from one of the small nomad tribes to the east of Midian! It would be better to get on the right side of this man—if he was one of them. "Let me fix you something to eat," he offered belatedly.

The man nodded.

But when Gideon came back with a basket of prepared veal, some unleavened cakes, and a little bowl of broth, the stranger pointed to a smooth, flat rock just beyond the oak tree. "Place it all on that rock."

Gideon, wondering at the strange order, did so. The wayfarer picked up the traveling staff lying in the grass beside him, and touched the rock with the point of his staff. In one flashing flare of flame fire came up out of the rock, and consumed the cakes and the broth and the meat. Paralyzed with fear, Gideon fell down on the ground, covered his eyes with his hands, and moaned down into the dirt of the yard, "Alas, Lord God, I have seen an angel face to face, now I will die."

The angel touched Gideon. "Do not be afraid, you shan't die."

But Gideon did not stir, and when at last he dared lift his face and peer through his fingers the angel was gone. The angel was gone, but was he—Gideon—still alive? He touched himself—he was alive. Gideon got up.

That night the spirit of God came upon Gideon. Moved by the spirit, in the middle of the night Gideon took ten of his father's slaves and led them to the grove and altar that Gideon's townspeople of Ophrah had erected to the heathen idol, Baal. With his men Gideon broke down the altar, and hacked down the bushes and trees of the grove. In his fervor and zeal for God, Gideon even took two of his father's bullocks out of hiding and sacrificed them to God—one on the rock of the angel under the oak, and one in the ruined grove of Baal. He had the men bring the hacked brush of the grove for firewood. They burned the whole grove, but strangely the flame and the burning went unnoticed that night by the townspeople of Ophrah.

In the morning the early worshipers of the idol of Baal came upon the destruction. Then the news flew. The whole town gathered. This was gross sacrilege—the townspeople were scandalized, horrified, terrified. What would their god, Baal, do? Who had done this to Baal? They ferreted it out; they beat the secret out of one of Gideon's ten men—Gideon, the son of Joash, had committed the terrible vandalism. A mob marched on the mountain home of Joash. When Gideon saw them coming, all his fine fervor for the Lord God of Israel was suddenly gone—gone in fear and trembling. He hid in his father's house.

Like a little boy he hid behind the skirts of his father's robes. His old father had to go out to face the outraged mob that had come to lynch Gideon. "Bring him out. Bring out Gideon."

Old Joash coolly stood his ground, coolly laughed. "Oh, you've come for Gideon. You've taken it on yourselves to fight Baal's battle for him? What's wrong with that god of yours? Can't he take care of Gideon himself? You ought to be ashamed—come here, a whole mob, with clubs and stones to put Gideon to death for your dead god. You have to fight with stones because your god is dead—himself a dead piece of stone. Some god. Some courage." And the old man laughed. His standing there quietly laughing brought some sense and some shame to the mob that confronted him; they threw away their stones and clubs, they dribbled away.

Gideon took courage from the fearlessness of his old father.

And when Gideon's fear left him, the spirit of God could come upon him again. Moved by the spirit, Gideon—he, who had been afraid of threshing out a bushel of wheat too loudly—boldly jumped up on a rock in the full view of the town of Ophrah, and blew the trumpet. Gideon blew the summoning trumpet until the whole town came out to him. Amazingly, they who before had come out to kill him now wanted to follow him, were willing to be his men and fight the mighty Midianites. The surprising success of his trumpeting made Gideon still bolder; he sent the townsmen as messengers through all of Manasseh, to Asher, to Zebulun, and even to the tribe of Naphtali. Again Gideon was surprised and astounded—the tribes rose as a man, and boldly came out to him in Ophrah.

It scared Gideon. He had not expected such an outpouring, such an army. And still they came. Now everything waited for him, depended on him. Gideon's fine fervor and high spirits dribbled away, he was frightened again. But there was no one to hide behind now. He had come out boldly, blown the summoning trumpet; the tribes had answered boldly. Now it was up to him.

Gideon secretly crept away to the empty winepress. Only the chaff from his threshing and an old, ragged, worn sheepskin fleece lay on the bare floor of the winepress. The quivering Gideon dropped down on the fleece, prayed, "God, give me a sign! Lord God of Israel, give me a sign that you still are with me, and that I am to free Israel from the Midianites."

He prayed, scared eyes wide open—scared eyes on the fleece on which he kneeled. Ah, that would have to be the sign—the fleece! "Lord God, be patient with me, and in the morning give me this sign. Let the ground and the floor be bone dry, but let this fleece be soaked with dew."

It was so the next morning. Barefooted in the morning darkness, Gideon stole out of the house with a bowl. The floor of the winepress was dry, the fleece was soaked through with dew. Gideon wrung it out above the bowl. The bowl filled, the water splashed on his bare feet.

Gideon looked up to heaven and to God, shook with excitement and awe and fervor. . . . Ah, no, it was fear—he was shaking with fear. "Lord God," he chattered, feet cold with the morning dew, "be patient with me, be patient, do not be angry with me, but I must ask one more sign. In the morning may the ground be wet, may the fleece be dry."

He stumbled away knowing that his whole request had been little more than a scared scheme to postpone making any decision still another day—to give him another day to hold off from leading his army down the mountains. The town was full of eager volunteers, the men were impatient to get on to the battle. God must be as impatient, Gideon thought miserably, as were the men who asked nothing but to be his soldiers.

It was so in the morning. In the winepress the chaff floated on dew, but the fleece lay in the midst of the wetness as dry as the hot sands of the Midianite desert.

Ah, God was patient, God was faithful. Now there was nothing more that Gideon could ask, dared to ask. The time had come—the time for decision. Before he could weaken again, in morning darkness, Gideon went out to his men gathered in the town of Ophrah. In morning darkness he started his army down the mountains toward the valley of the Midianites. He mustered his men on the march. They brought Gideon the count of the muster, and Gideon's courage and confidence leaped—thirty-two thousand men! But it also shamed Gideon. Everything had gone so well, everybody was so eager. These marching men had been fretting and waiting for him these days, while he had to have secret, little private miracles performed for him by God to give him a little courage and assurance. But now the long snaking columns marched behind him down the twisting mountain road. He—Gideon—a general at the head of thirty-two thousand fighting men! Was it only a week ago that he had been beating out some green wheat to hide a few bushels from the Midianites? Now at the head of thirty-two thousand men, he was on his way to destroy the Midianites.

At last came the noonday break. Then men rested along the roadside. Gideon went off by himself to ponder plans and battle schemes, but he felt inexperienced, incompetent. Then at high noon in the blazing sun the word of God came to the baffled Gideon.

"Too many men. . . . You have far too many men. If you go into battle with these thirty-two thousand, Israel will take the credit. Israel will boast—we did it with our mighty army. We saved Israel. Now then, announce to the men that whoever is frightened or timid—that man may go home."

Gideon was astounded and dismayed. But as he walked back to the companies stretched along the road, he took heart, reassured himself. These eager volunteers go home? Afraid? They'd hardly been able to wait for him to get ready. And all morning they'd eagerly marched along at top speed.

The men lounging along the road saw Gideon come, and pushed to their feet. They didn't even wait for Gideon to give the order. The orders went up the road from mouth to mouth and company to company, and the men arranged themselves in the middle of the road, ready to resume the march.

Gideon stepped before the lead company, his own company, his townsmen. "Any of you within hearing of my voice —and pass the word along to the companies behind you—any of you, oh, a bit timid, a bit sorry you've come now that we're getting closer to the Midianite camp—well, if you don't feel so warlike any more—any of you, for any reason at all, that would rather go back home. . . . You may go home. Now!"

Gideon waited confidently, a slight smile on his face as he watched the surprised volunteers mouth his words to each other. They called out the strange order to the companies behind them. The words traveled over and over up the long twisting road.

Gideon waited. The movement must have begun with the end companies far out of sight behind the turns in the road, but gradually it reached the companies within Gideon's view, and then at last it hit the company of Gideon's own townsmen standing directly before him. . . . They turned! Without embarrassment, explanation, or shame, they left. They turned, peeled off from the ranks, marched away up the mountain road to go back home.

Gideon and the remaining men stood staring in open-mouthed unbelief. But the columns of the cowards swelled and grew. From a single file it became a parade—the parade of the marching cowards, hurrying back home. The thin column remaining in the middle of the road thinned some more. The deserters called to them, waved to them jauntily, and more men hastily squeezed out of the ranks and ran after the deserters—deserters themselves.

They ran off. They were shameless!

The speechless Gideon stood there, gave no orders, made no effort to restrain a single deserter. But somehow, strangely, he felt comforted, encouraged—at least he'd been cowardly in secret, and only before his God—these men didn't care who knew!

The thinned companies stood quietly in the road—subdued—the men who remained more hushed and shamed than the deserters who left.

"Now close ranks, muster the men, and count what's left," Gideon ordered at last.

Again they brought Gideon the count of the new muster. "Only ten thousand left—twenty-two thousand deserted."

"Forward march," Gideon ordered.

The thin ranks swung into step behind him. The march down to the valley began, the march quickened. Gideon set the pace, and for some reason he felt better, surer of himself, emboldened. At least, he even comforted himself, in his inexperience it was better to be responsible for the lives of ten thousand than for thirty-two thousand.

In the heat of the day, in the late afternoon, they came to the foot of the mountains, and to a small mountain stream as it slowed and curled into the valley. Gideon gave the order, and the men rested. But Gideon went off by himself, once more to plot battle plans—this time for only ten thousand men. But the word of God again came to Gideon.

"Too many men. You still have too many men—far too many. Give them the order to fall out and drink at the brook, and have them watched at their drinking. Separate all those who get down on their knees and suck up the water from those who hunch down, scoop up water with their hands, and drink from their hands. Keep only those. Send the rest home."

Gideon gave the order. There were only three hundred men that drank from their hands. Nine thousand seven hundred men had to be sent home.

But these were no willing deserters. Their captains marched them away, but the big company of over nine thousand men was resentful, they fumed and muttered rebelliously among themselves. Gideon with the little group of three hundred stood looking forlornly after them.

Suddenly Gideon ordered them back. They came back eagerly. Gideon was forced to explain. "Men, I called you back, but don't misunderstand—it's not for battle. Men, I don't understand this any more than you do. Nor is this my idea at all—God ordered it! When you drank from the brook, that was God's test. With only those few that drank from their hands God wants to destroy Midian." Gideon waved his hand helplessly toward the endless miles of tents stretched over the flat of the plain. "But how with only three hundred men can I begin the battle? With only three hundred it will have to be an endless struggle, so you nine thousand—will you leave these three hundred men your victuals? And your trumpets and pitchers and lamps? At least enough of them so each man of the three hundred will have a trumpet, and pitcher, and lamp?"

Mystified by Gideon's odd request, the nine thousand obediently piled their belongings before Gideon, then silently began the march back up the mountains. Gideon stared down at the trumpets and pitchers and lamps piled at his feet as if to draw some comfort, some security from the strange, mixed-up pile.

"Now that we've drunk, we'd better eat," he quietly told the three hundred. The men silently sorted out the food from among the lamps and the pitchers, silently munched the food, and stared at the thousands of tents of the Midianites in the valley. From time to time they glanced at Gideon as if asking for an explanation, but Gideon had no explanation to give, didn't understand now why he had suddenly requested the lamps and the trumpets and pitchers. He looked again at the mixed-up pile—three hundred men with three hundred crockery pitchers, and there must be at least a hundred and fifty thousand Midianites down in that camp. . . .

Night fell, as night must, and the time for decision came, as a time for decision must come, and still Gideon didn't have the slightest beginning of a battle plan for his pitiful little army of three hundred. What plans could he make for three hundred men with three hundred pitchers—well, they had their swords, three hundred swords against a hundred thousand Midianite swords. God had willed it so, but Gideon sat staring into the darkness with little will and no plan, and no confidence or understanding.

The word of the Lord came to Gideon.

"Creep into the camp of the Midianites. And if you haven't the courage to do it alone, take your own personal slave with you. There in the camp of the Midianites I will give you a sign, and I will give you courage."

Gideon and his servant waited at the edge of the great camp until the time of the changing of the watch. Then, as the watch changed, he and the servant slid on their bellies toward the shadowy darkness of the nearest Midianite tent. They lay breathless as a sentry came pacing by. The sentry stopped just beyond them, turned his head toward the tent, stood listening.

To Gideon's dismay somebody inside the tent began muttering, then the Midianite cried out in his sleep. The Midianite must have wakened another soldier in the tent. There was talk.

"What's wrong with you?"

"Oh, I guess I was dreaming. It was horrible! Mind you, I was dreaming—of all things—that a loaf of barley bread came rolling down the mountains into our camp. And it hit our tent, and that little loaf knocked our tent over, and our tent knocked down the next one and down went the tents

—you know how things go on and on in that kind of a scary dream."

Gideon could hear the man take a deep breath—glad he was awake from the dream.

"You know what that dream means, don't you?" said the other, knowing voice. "I understand dreams and there've been rumors that some man named Gideon has got together a big army of Israelites. That's what it means—that loaf of barley bread of yours knocking down our whole camp. That loaf is Gideon and his army. It's the sword of Gideon over us. And the tents all going down—that means we're going down before Gideon. We're lost."

"Aw, go back to sleep," the first voice said with a yawn. "You're worse than my dream." The man laughed. "I'd better catch a few winks myself before all that happens."

The sentry had gone on. The voices in the tent were silent. But outside the tent Gideon kneeled and prayed to his God—prayed a wordless prayer of thanksgiving. God had given him this sign, now at last he knew, now he understood—the battle was the Lord's. And now he even had a battle plan, for now he understood the sudden impulse—it must have been the spirit of God—that had made him ask the big company to furnish him the trumpets, lamps, and pitchers.

Gideon and the servant crawled out of the camp, hustled back to the three hundred.

"Up," Gideon ordered. "Up now, for now I know that God has delivered the host of Midian into our hands."

He hurriedly divided the three hundred into three companies of a hundred men. He ordered each man to equip himself with a trumpet in one hand, and an empty pitcher with an unlit lamp in the empty pitcher in the other hand. He ordered each company of one hundred to a different side of the huge camp of the Midianites. "Do what you hear me and my company do," he instructed. "When I blow the trumpet, smash your crockery pitcher against the next man's pitcher, make the biggest noise you can. Then light your lamps. Take the lamp in your left hand, your trumpet in your right hand, and blow the trumpets, and shout with all your might, 'The sword of the Lord and of Gideon.' "

"And that is all?" the captain of one of the little companies of one hundred asked.

"That is all," Gideon said. "It is all that is needed. God has put the fear and terror of the sword of Gideon into their hearts. That is why I want you to shout about the sword of Gideon. The crash of pitchers and the blast of trumpets will scare them awake—the lights ranging on three sides of the camp will confuse them. But that is absolutely all you do, stand and smash your pitchers, light your lamps, blow your trumpets, and shout about swords—never mind pulling your real swords. They won't be needed—leave it to God. This battle is the Lord's."

In black darkness Gideon and his company waited until the other two little companies had time to take up their positions. The camp of the Midianites lay in deep, dark sleep. The watch had been changed again; only the few sentries were

awake shuffling lone and dark around the outside of the camp, trying to avoid the stretched ropes of the tents in the night blackness. There wasn't a sound, except the slight scuffle the sentries' feet made in the sand. The dark clump of Gideon's little company was part of the darkness and the silence. Slowly Gideon lifted his trumpet.

Then there it came—a lone, short, startling trumpet blast. At the blast of the trumpet the pitchers of Gideon's own company smashed together in a fearful crashing sound. The two companies on the other sides of the camp took it up. The crashing and shouting and trumpeting seemed to be all around the camp. The shouts of men mingled queerly with the crashing and the trumpeting.

"The sword of the Lord and of Gideon!"

It was as if an earthquake struck the camp of the Midianites. The tents shook. Tents quivered, tents wallowed in a great upheaval of panic. The tents shook with the panic and struggle that went on inside of them. In the darkness, in their panic, in the startling terror of their awakening, and the sudden nearness of the trumpets and shouts, it seemed to the Midianites that the Israelites were storming their tents, were already inside the tents in a total surprise raid. Confused tentmate rose up against tentmate, soldier fought soldier, Midianite against Midianite. In screaming horror of mortal hand-to-hand combat, they grabbed swords in the panic in which they had come up out of sleep. They died, coming up out of sleep. They screamed out of sleep into sudden death, pierced and slashed by the swords of their own tentmates.

They fought—the host of Midian—but not with Gideon

and his three little bands. They madly, insanely fought each other, and the clash and the scream and the shrill of battle was in all the tents. The tents went down, the tents bowled over as soldier rolled over soldier, wrestling each other, choking each other with bare hands. They thrust swords wildly through anything that came near, anything that moved or stirred in the darkness, anything at all that made a sound. The tents went down, tent falling over tent. And still the smothered cries and smothered struggles went on in the fallen tents. Streets of tents went down in a horrible mass of struggling.

On and on the trumpets blew. The trumpet sounds, the horrifying shouts of the Israelites seemed everywhere—the flaming light of the Israelite lamps beyond the darkness under the smothering tents.

The smash and the cry and the shriek of the battle inside the tents, as a hundred and twenty thousand men battled and destroyed each other, resounded through the valley and climbed up the mountains. The rejected nine thousand of Gideon turned and stormed down the mountain back to the Midianite camp. Up in the mountains the twenty-two thousand pathetic deserters on their way home also took heart from the great sounds of battle, and started down the mountains to the valley of the Midianites.

But in the valley the battle was over as it began. There remained only the pursuit of the pitiful remnant who had escaped the massacre inside the tents. The battle was over before the returning Israelites could begin it. The battle and the victory were the Lord's.

THE TRUMPET OF VICTORY

And the children of Ammon oppressed the children of Israel eighteen years—all the children of Israel that were on the other side of Jordan in Gilead.

And the people of Gilead said one to another, "What man is he that will begin to fight against the children of Ammon? He shall be head over all the inhabitants of Gilead." . . . And the elders of Israel went to fetch Jephtha out of the land of Tob, and they said unto Jephtha, "Come and be our captain, that we may fight with the children of Ammon."

Then Jephtha went with the elders of Israel, and the people made him head and captain over them, and Jephtha uttered all his words before the Lord. And Jephtha vowed a vow unto the Lord, and said, "If thou shalt deliver the children of Ammon into mine hands, then it shall be that whatsoever cometh forth of the doors of my house to meet me, when I return in victory, shall surely be the Lord's, and I will offer it up for an offering."

And he smote the children of Ammon from Aroer, even till thou come to Minnith, even twenty cities, and unto the plain of the vineyards, with a very great slaughter.

From JUDGES 10 & 11

IT WAS over, it was done. The battle was won, the victory was complete. Jephtha and his band of men were back in the mountains—back almost at the same spot on the high little mountain road from where they had started the battle against Ammon. Eighteen years Ammon had enslaved and oppressed Israel, but now in one day it was over, freedom was won for all in the whole land of Israel.

Oh, Jephtha and his raiders had not done it alone, but they had started it. It had begun with them. One band of raiders starting almost from the spot where they now again stood. Seeing Jephtha and his band going into battle with the whole terrible, well-armed country of Ammon, the Israelites had come rushing to join Jephtha.

There now far away, far down the mountain, lay Ammon and its valley and its twenty towns. A smoke and burning went up from the valley, smoke from the twenty towns. Even the vineyards lay in smoldering ruin. It was complete, the victory was complete—in one long terrible day.

Even the return march, the victory march, was over—except for Jephtha and his men, and for them nothing more remained but the march through the mountains back to Mizpeh, the town where Jephtha and his raiders lived. Jephtha lived in the outskirts of Mizpeh in a little house with a small pasture cupped in the mountains for his cow, his small flock of goats and sheep, and three horses and a donkey.

Now as the little band stood alone again at the point from which the battle had begun in the early morning, Jephtha at their head stood looking at the faraway destruction, but his thoughts were of his own little farm. As he and his band had marched back in victory at the head of the columns, the men from the tribes of Israel who had come to join them in the morning—was it still the same long day?—had left them as easily as they had joined them, each man peeling away from the long marching column, and going home. Home—

only they who'd begun the battle were still far away from home! Jephtha stood so long, thinking and looking, some of his men began to throw themselves down in the road.

The trumpeter of the band eased himself down, settled his back against the rock wall of the mountain, carefully laid his precious trumpet down beside him, and also looked at the smoke and the burning. His lips moved as he counted. "Count them, Jephtha—twenty burnings! Twenty towns that are nothing but smoke pots now. All in one day!" He grabbed up his trumpet and excitedly blew a long blast toward the burning.

The trumpeter's victory trumpeting ran through the mountains and was cast back from the rocks until trumpets seemed to sound all around. The sound rolled away in the valley, and the trumpeter stopped. He threw himself full length along the foot of the rock wall, and, wiping his lips, told Jephtha, "As for me, I'm done. It's still the same day, I guess, but it's been the longest day of my life. We've marched and fought all day, we went the farthest, we fought the longest, the others have all gone home—let's camp here and march home fresh in the morning."

The men lying along the road muttered weary approval.

But it was as if a restlessness had come over Jephtha with the trumpeter's trumpeting—a victory restlessness. He looked at the trumpeter almost in surprise and unbelief. He looked at his men lying along the road. "It's always seemed to me that victory isn't victory until you bring it home. All the others went home. I'll wager they're sitting home now—soaking their tired feet, their wives dressing their wounds, the children bringing them food, and all the villagers gathered around to hear the news of the victory from the lips of the heroes."

"Listen to him," the trumpeter said. "He's homesick. And all he's got is just a daughter. Well, it looks like the poor girl all by herself will have to surround him, soak his feet and bring him food and listen to his hero talk."

Jephtha grinned. "Don't forget my donkey! . . . But don't tell me—sure we marched the farthest and fought the longest, but we're supposed to be tough, hard men. You're not going to sit there and tell me that all those others could make it home—but not Jephtha's raiders."

The trumpeter picked up his trumpet and heaved himself to his feet. "He's right," he said to the men, "I can't stay here either. He's right—victory isn't victory until you take it home. Let's go home and soak our feet."

The band struggled up, but Jephtha seemed to have to take one last look at the burning in the valley. "Eighteen years," he said softly. "Eighteen years of slavery and terror and in one day God gives the victory." He turned to his men. "You know, men, what I was thinking of when I stood looking down on that ruin? Of my donkey!"

The men started laughing, but Jephtha remained serious. "You know how he'll be—standing there lazy and half asleep in his stall at the back of the house. But somehow he always seems to know when I'm coming home. And even if I'm still a mile away—he knows, and he backs off his stall and pushes the back door of the house open and runs to hang his big heavy head over the stone wall along the road to have it ready for me to scratch that round, itchy spot on his forehead. It's right between the ears—just a little below—but when I scratch it my little donkey goes to heaven. He almost faints."

Jephtha spread his hands toward the destruction. "All that slaughter, and all I can think of is my donkey."

The men stood grinning, for, tough as he was, they all knew what a fool Jephtha made himself over his little pet donkey.

"No, men," Jephtha said. "It's not just the donkey. I was remembering the vow I made—if God gave me the victory and I returned home victorious, I would sacrifice the first thing that came out of my house to meet me. And I suddenly knew it had to be the little donkey. Look at the victory! What would it mean if I sacrificed a sheep or a goat, or even my one cow? But my little donkey that goes to heaven when I scratch him between his ears—that would go deep, that would hurt. I've killed my share of men today, but that would hurt. But eighteen years, and in one day the amazing victory! That's why I've still got to rush home this same day to fulfill my vow I made to God, and that's why it's got to be the donkey. If you can't come with me, I'll go on alone. But we started this together, I'd like to have you with me for the victory sacrifice."

"Get going," one of the men said gruffly. "We're right on your heels."

Jephtha turned and strode away along the mountain road, and his weary band fell in behind him.

But the feet were heavy, and the road high, and the day had been too long. The heavy feet—hips, legs, and feet—

would not swing along in the heavy sand that the mountain had funneled into the narrow, deep road. Hip, leg, and foot could no longer swing along with the highhearted feeling of victory. Only Jephtha seemed tireless, and he set the pace. He strode eager and excited and at such a pace men began falling out to rest at the roadside.

The little town of Mizpeh and its roofs came into sight far below them in the sleepy evening shadows of the mountains, but still men had to fall out. They stumbled to the side of the road and threw themselves down, unable to walk one more step.

Jephtha strode on, as if unaware of his struggling band, for he had a high mission, a high, sacred duty still to perform—he who had opened his mouth to the Lord and vowed a great vow.

And then—always it came suddenly—there right below Jephtha around a sharp turn in the mountain road lay his own little house in the cup of its valley. Straight down below him lay the pasture, the goats and sheep dotting it, the cow serene, the three black horses three dark shadows against the mountain wall at the far side of the little cupped pasture. Jephtha plunged on.

Behind Jephtha, around the hairpin turn, now came the sturdy trumpeter, and only about twelve other men behind him—all the rest had fallen by the wayside. But as he came striding around the turn, the trumpeter's legs suddenly failed him. He wobbled toward the side of the road, started to throw himself down. It became more of a falling than a throwing, the wind was knocked out of him, but he remembered to hold his trumpet high and safe as he fell. The trumpeter groaned his disgust, lay muttering.

Jephtha turned. "Not you—trumpeter. And I thought you were the toughest of us all. But did you have to go down a hundred paces short of the town? And here I'd counted on you to blow the trumpet and wake up Mizpeh—make them rush out to see their heroes come home."

The trumpeter looked up at Jephtha. "Don't make me feel more ashamed than I am. I'd counted on doing the same thing myself." He looked down at Jephtha's pasture. Suddenly he rolled over on his back, brought the trumpet to his lips, and, pointing it straight into the darkening sky, tried trumpeting with his last weary breath. He tried again, and then at last managed a victory blast that resounded through the mountain and fell down on the little pasture. "Well, that's it," he told Jephtha. "With all the wind knocked out of me that's the best I can do—blow victory to your cow and horses."

Jephtha grinned and marched off. He marched along the pasture, saw his animals stand rigid and listening. From behind him there still came a second long trumpet blast. The cow in the corner of the pasture lifted her feet and began prancing. The three horses, whiplashing their tails, stormed toward the stone wall along the mountain road. Goats and sheep stood, heads lifted, and one goat reared up and danced among them on hind legs.

But Jephtha started to run. At the second sound of the trumpet the back door of his house had burst open—there now came the little donkey galloping on mincing steps toward the front of the house and the stone wall.

In the turn of the road the trumpeter must have seen Jephtha running, must have seen the donkey galloping toward the stone wall. And knowing that that was what Jephtha had wanted—the donkey to be the first thing to meet him out of his house—the trumpeter must have managed to blow a last excited blast of triumph.

But at that last short blast, the donkey stopped still. Stopped beside the house and stood still in absolute, immovable donkey stubbornness.

As the donkey stopped, the door at the front of the house burst open, a whole bevy of girls came storming through the door, and Jephtha's own daughter was ahead of them all. The girls came running, half dancing, came wildly shaking tabrets and timbrels—the news of the victory must have got to Mizpeh—the girls must have waited inside the house with Jephtha's daughter to surprise and meet him with a victory dance. Jephtha stood as if turned to stone. But his daughter ran into the road, hurled herself toward her father. Now the little donkey came mincing toward the road. The donkey hung his head over the wall.

In the road Jephtha's anguished hands grabbled at his clothes, tore them. It was as if he couldn't move. His daughter flung herself up at him, but Jephtha didn't hold her, didn't put arms around her. He fell away from her as if she'd been a vile leper. Horrified words squeezed out of his throat. "I opened my mouth," he whispered hoarsely. "Oh, my daughter, I opened my mouth to the Lord, and I swore an oath that if God gave me the victory, I would sacrifice the first thing that came out of my house to meet me. . . ."

The girl swayed in the road. Jephtha had to grab her to keep her from falling. They clung to each other, but they could find no words. The twelve men of the band came up, stood silent and stony. The girls stood with their timbrels and tabrets. A girl began crying. Jephtha's daughter turned her head away from her father, looked at the weeping girl. "If you opened your mouth to the Lord, oh, my father, for this mighty victory, then the vow you vowed was part of the victory, and then I am part of your victory, too." Her voice faltered. "Father, could you give me two months—two months in the mountains? Just me and these my girl friends—to remember my lost youth up in the mountains? Two months, Father, is all I ask. Then I'll come back, and you can do with me according to the vow you vowed unto the Lord."

Jephtha violently shook his head.

His daughter turned to her companions. "Will you go with me?"

They nodded their heads; they were crying. Jephtha's daughter looked up at him, as if for permission. Jephtha again shook his head, but then he managed one word. "Go," he said.

Ahead of her companions Jephtha's daughter strode up the mountain, up the same road down which her father had come. She strode ahead of the softly weeping girls, their timbrels and tabrets silent. There was no sound. Then there was a sharp rattling sound as the anguished trumpeter, realizing what he had done with that last blast of the trumpet, crashed the trumpet down on his knee, flung the broken, bent trumpet down into the pasture among the goats and sheep and horses.

The banging, clattering trumpet scattered them. The trumpeter slunk away in the shadows.

But ahead of the weeping maidens the daughter of Jephtha went up toward the trumpeter, and up to the mountains as if hearing and seeing none of it at all. As if for her trumpets were still blowing victory up in the mountains—as if victory was all around. As if in two months she would not have to come back down this selfsame road—come back to her anguished father who would have to sacrifice his daughter in accordance with his vow—he, who had opened his mouth to the Lord.

THE PHILISTINES UPON YOU

And the children of Israel did evil in the sight of the Lord; and the Lord delivered them into the hand of the Philistines.

And there was a certain woman of Zorah. And the angel of the Lord appeared unto the woman and said unto her, "Lo, thou shalt bear a son; and no razor shall come on his head: for the child shall be a Nazarite unto God: and he shall begin to deliver Israel out of the hand of the Philistines."

And the woman bore a son, and called his name Samson: and the child grew, and the Lord blessed him. And the Spirit of the Lord began to move him at times. . . .

And it came to pass afterward that Samson loved a woman in the valley of Sorek, whose name was Delilah. And the lords of the Philistines came up unto her, and said unto her, "Entice him, and see wherein his great strength lieth, that we may bind him to afflict him: and we will give thee every one of us eleven hundred pieces of silver."

And Delilah said to Samson, "Tell me, I pray thee, wherein thy great strength lieth, and wherewith thou mightest be bound to afflict thee."

And Samson said unto her, "If they bind me with seven green withes that were never dried, then shall I be weak, and be as another man."

And she bound him with them. And she said unto him, "The Philistines be upon thee, Samson."

And he broke the withes as a thread of tow is broken when it toucheth the fire. So his strength was not known.

And Delilah said unto Samson, "Behold, thou hast

mocked me, now tell me, I pray thee, wherewith thou mightest be bound."

And he said unto her, "If they bind me fast with new ropes, then shall I be weak, and be as another man."

Delilah therefore took new ropes, and bound him therewith, and said unto him, "The Philistines be upon thee, Samson."

And he broke them from off his arms like a thread.

And Delilah said unto Samson, "Hitherto thou hast mocked me, tell me wherewith thou mightest be bound."

And he said unto her, "If thou weavest the seven locks of my head with the web."

And she fastened it with the pin, and said unto him, "The Philistines be upon thee, Samson."

And he awaked out of his sleep, and went away with the pin of the beam, and with the web.

And Delilah said unto him, "How canst thou say, 'I love thee,' when thine heart is not with me? Thou hast mocked me these three times. . . ."

And it came to pass, when she pressed him daily, and urged him, so that his soul was vexed unto death, that he told her all his heart, and said, "There hath not come a razor upon mine head, for I have been a Nazarite unto God. If I be shaven, then my strength will go from me, and I shall become weak, and be like any other man."

And when Delilah saw that he had told her all his heart, she sent and called for the lords of the Philistines.

Then the lords of the Philistines came up unto her, and brought money in their hand. And she made Samson to sleep upon her knees; and she called for a man, and she caused him to shave off the seven locks of his head. And she said, "The Philistines be upon thee, Samson."

And he awoke out of his sleep, and said, "I will go out as at other times before, and shake myself."

And he wist not that the Lord was departed from him.

From JUDGES 13 & 16

NOW then there wasn't much left to his life. Samson's life was grinding away, it seemed, in the heavy, dreary grinding of the upper millstone on the nether millstone—life was wearing away in the weary, dry sound of the grain crushing between the two millstones. Yes, now his life was grinding to its hopeless, useless, wasteful end.

The Philistines had dug out his eyes, and they'd given him the work of a dumb ox to do—turning the heavy grist mill was the work of an ox. Before Samson they had used a blind ox—so the boy said—blind oxen were better for going around and around the mill, they didn't get dizzy. Now the Philistines used him—Samson—he was blind.

To show their contempt for his harmlessness, they let him grind at the mill in the open courtyard of the prison. Where could he go without eyes? And to further grind him down with their contempt, they had given him a small boy for a keeper. When Samson felt for him and occasionally laid his hand on the boy's head, the lad didn't seem to reach much higher than his knees. Of course, he was a big man, a big ox now, a big, blind ox. Stumble on, find the deep, worn-down path made around the mill by the ox before him, feel with his bare feet, put one heavy foot before the other in the groove of the ox path, turn the heavy mill to the grinding, weary sound of the grain cracking and crushing—it was his life, the life they had left him.

At least, the pain was gone from the hollow sockets of his eyes. No pain, and no tears—they hadn't even left him his tear ducts when they had torn out his eyes. But there would have been no tears had there been tear ducts—only blind disgust with himself. Oh, surely, Delilah, the woman he had loved, had foully betrayed him, but he had betrayed his God.

No, no tears, and no pain any more, although his blindness was still recent enough that he needed the little boy to lead him, except when he put foot after foot in the deep, smooth path of the ox. But he was weary—oh, so weary. The torture had weakened him, the great muscles were not what they once had been. Still, the last few days it had seemed to him that some of his strength was coming back—the strength of an ox, good enough to turn a mill—the strength of the lion was gone. Suddenly Samson shook his head as he lifted hollow eyes to the warm sun in the sky and prayed wordlessly to his God—lips moving—that he might once again, oh, just once, feel the swish of the locks of his hair against his neck. He did not toss his head again, the boy keeper might be watching. His hair was growing, his strength was coming back. But it took so long for hair to grow after they'd shaved you bald—much longer for hair to grow again than for pain to go out of gone eyes.

Samson suddenly listened for any sound of his boy keeper. He thought he heard the stealthy approach of feet—but many feet. Now there was a stifled, scared giggle as the feet stole closer. Samson knew what was coming. A gang of Philistine boys was sneaking up on him. Now there was a moment's quiet, and then they yelled it at him, all together:

"Samson, the Philistines upon you!"

The words of Delilah with which she'd betrayed him!

Now there was the wild, panicky scattering and rush of feet as they scrambled beyond the reach of Samson's length of brass chain. And now the boy keeper yelled after them, "Get out of here! You're not supposed to come in here."

Samson understood—for all his yelling now, the boy keeper had been one of them. Proud of being Samson's keeper, he couldn't resist showing off to his playmates. Ah, the children of the Philistines were still scared of him—he'd been the Philistines' bogeyman all his life. Samson—the name with which the mothers of Philistia had scared their children into behaving.

But now the Philistine children yelled the words of Delilah at him. The words with which Delilah had betrayed him had become a street call and a byword in Philistia. Samson's hands cramped around the thick pole of the grindstone in shame and remorse. For a moment he rested his forehead on the thick pole.

The boy keeper came back alone. "Samson," he said, "I'm sorry—I really am. I didn't see that gang come, or I wouldn't have let them mock you. . . . But you've got to keep turning the mill. You know you mayn't stand still."

"I know," Samson said quietly.

"As soon as there are a few moments when nobody's around," the boy whispered, "I'll let you know, and then you can rest a while."

"Thank you, son," Samson said. "May I have a little water?"

When the boy walked away to the water bucket, Samson lifted his sightless face to the sun. "Lord God of Israel, make my hair grow again—give me back my strength again, if it be for just a few moments. . . ."

Didn't they notice? Didn't they see it? Didn't it fairly scream out at them—they with eyes in their heads—that God was answering prayer? That the great, mighty God of Israel and of foolish Samson had remembered him at the grinding mill? His hair was growing out! Thank God, they noticed nothing. God must have blinded the Philistines, too. Didn't they know that as his hair grew his strength grew? Didn't they remember what they had learned from Delilah?

They noticed nothing. They still walked down the street of the prison yelling catcalls, having fun shouting out the popular phrase that must be known throughout all Philistia —the words of Delilah:

"Samson, the Philistines upon you. The Philistines upon you, Samson."

After the empty words came the empty laugh. But the words no longer touched Samson—not now in his new strength. He only worried about the length of his hair—that they might notice. He no longer tossed his head for fear the boy keeper might see the lengthening hair. He tried to remember to be tired and weak, and to ask often for water. He turned the mill so slowly and weakly, the boy had to warn him when an important Philistine came along.

They'd made up a secret signal—he and the boy. They'd made a joke between them of the Delilah street call. Now Samson could laugh and joke about it in his growing strength!

To warn him that there were important Philistines watching, the boy would yell at him, "Samson, the Philistines upon you." Groaning and staggering weakly, Samson would turn the mill a little faster—a pitiful, weak, blind man.

"Ah, son," Samson told the boy, "you are good to me. And even though you're a Philistine, I won't forget and I'll be good to you."

"Just don't get me in trouble and turn the mill a little faster," the boy said.

But then one day there was the noise of hammering and of voices and of sawing in the courtyard of the prison. Busy sounds, heavy pounding. "What are they doing now?" Samson asked the boy without stopping the mill.

"Oh, they're building a high fence around you. Too many people are making it a habit to go round by way of the street of the prison to show you off to strangers and visitors. They want it stopped. You're going to be the main attraction at the coming festival—they want to save you for that."

"What festival?"

"Why, the dedication of the great new temple to our god, Dagon. Hadn't you heard? The town is getting full of people. They're coming from all over Philistia. . . . Why, it's the architectural marvel of the age," the boy recited as if from something he'd read or heard, or carefully memorized from his elders. "Everybody's talking about it. That whole big temple is built in such a way that everything rests on just two big pillars in the middle. The pillars are right in the middle, but they hold up the whole upper structure. It's something new that's been invented by our best architect."

"And just what have I got to do with all that?" Samson asked.

"Well, it's not only that they're going to dedicate the new temple, it's also going to be in honor of our great god, Dagon, for delivering you into our hands. So you have to be there. That's why they're building the fence around you, so everybody won't see you first. . . . Hey, the Philistines upon you, Samson! Get going," the boy whispered urgently. "There's some important men come to see about the fence."

The next day the fence was finished. Samson and the boy were alone again in the courtyard of the prison. Although, according to the boy, people had already poked out the knots in the board fence, and were peeking at Samson through the knotholes. A dead fish came flying.

"With the high fence they feel pretty brave now, and not a bit scared of you, Samson," the boy said, kicking the dead fish aside. But then he shoved a small harp into Samson's hand.

Samson felt around the edges of the harp. "What is it?"

"The orders are you've got to learn to play this harp for the day of dedication of the temple to Dagon."

"But this is a toy harp—a monkey harp—the kind of a little harp that street players have trained monkeys bang away on."

"Yes, Samson," the boy said.

"First an ox, and now an ape," Samson said bitterly, and

made as if to fling the harp over the high fence that he could not see.

The boy grabbed his hand. "Please, Samson. . . . You'll get me in trouble. . . ."

"Yes, sorry," Samson said. "And what do I play on this silly harp?"

"The song of Delilah."

"The song of Delilah? What do you mean?"

"Haven't you heard them singing it? It's just come out, and everybody's singing and whistling and humming it. Somebody wrote it for the day of dedication, but they're already singing it in the streets. And I have to teach you the words, because you're going to sing them in the temple of Dagon. . . . It won't be hard—the words are about the same over and over. The song tells all the tricks Delilah played on you, and then after each trick you sing out real loud the words of Delilah—they make the chorus:

"The Philistines upon you, Samson.
Samson, the Philistines upon you."

"No!" Samson said.

"I haven't learned it all myself yet," the boy said anxiously, "and they didn't give me the words with the harp, so I suppose you'd first better learn to play the harp. It's got five strings. . . . Please, Samson, it'll be a break from walking around that mill all day long. It's easy work—it'll be easy."

Samson's hand cramped around the harp, and the sweat

broke out on his face. He remembered just in time—forced his hand to relax. The boy was standing right before him—he mustn't crush the toy to a wad in his hand. "Easy," he said hoarsely. "Yes, it should be easy. I suppose Delilah will be there, too, the day of the dedication of the temple to your fish god."

"I would almost think so," the boy said innocently. "Everybody that is anybody will be there—all the lords and rulers and princes. And Delilah is our national heroine now—why do you suppose they're making songs about her and you? I think, Samson, the idea is, they're going to have you up on the roof of the temple with the lords and the princes, and you're going to play the harp and accompany yourself as you sing the song about you and Delilah to Delilah. They say that's going to be the high point of the day. . . ." The boy stopped, Samson's face was working. "But that's only what they're saying," the boy said hastily. Then he added sullenly, "What did you expect, mercy? All these years you did with us as you pleased—you showed us no mercy. And now you're at our mercy."

Samson bowed his head.

"The Philistines upon you, Samson!" the boy suddenly warned. "Yes," he said loudly, "that's how the chorus goes. I'll try to get the words of the verses tomorrow. Now you'd better practice some more on the harp. Run your fingers over the strings—feel it? They're different lengths. I'll try to explain how each one has to be fingered."

Obedient to the warning, Samson gently, carefully plucked the harp, plunked out some small tinny sounds. But he lifted his face as he plunked, and his eyeless, empty sockets searched the sunless sky, as if searching for God, who had forsaken him, because he had forsaken God for the woman, Delilah. Then, afraid of the watchers the boy had warned of, he said almost soundlessly, "So Delilah will be there too. Well, I'll do my best to learn to play this harp. I'll sing my best to Delilah."

"Good," the boy said. "It's better than turning the mill."

Samson strummed the harp.

"That's right. Gently, gently, Samson. You look about as clumsy as an ox with the little harp. But maybe that's all right. Maybe that makes it better—the clumsier, the funnier it'll be."

"Very funny," Samson said between his teeth. "Plunk, plunk, plunk—and they'll fall down laughing. Maybe they'll fall all over me. . . . Maybe the song is right, son, maybe the Philistines will be upon me. Let's learn it well—maybe I can play them a tune." He laughed softly as if it were a real joke, laughed and tilted his head back against the upper millstone, rubbed his head back and forth as if he were thoroughly enjoying his own little joke. Ah, but he could feel his growing locks rubbing against the rough stone—he could hear it. It was music. God was good.

They hadn't bathed him, they hadn't let him bathe. They hadn't as much as let him wash his face. Maybe it was just as well; this way they might not notice the length of his matted hair.

Straight from the grinding mill in the prison, in the soiled, mean rags he wore, they'd taken him to the temple of Dagon —on bare feet, bare dirty feet from stumbling around in the ox rut around the grist mill. Taken him! They hadn't done him that honor. No company of soldiers had marched him to the temple. They'd let him come through the streets barefooted, carrying the toy harp in one hand, held by the other hand by his little boy keeper.

Samson stumbled awkwardly up the great wide stone stairway to the temple of Dagon. The boy guided him up the unknown steps. The great temple must be crowded to the rafters and the roof. A babble and excitement of voices was all around him and above him; it came from everywhere.

But they made room for the blind giant as he slowly came up the many steps. Before him, around him, and beside him the voices briefly fell silent as the crowd looked in awe at the great, hulking man, the terror and scourge of all Philistia. But when they saw the bare feet and the matted hair and the rags and the little toy harp so foolish in his big hand, the voices closed in behind Samson again—not awed, not scared any more. The jokes and the wisecracks and catcalls came trooping up the steps after Samson, first hushed, then louder. Behind him voices boldly repeated the Delilah song to each other. "The Philistines upon you, Samson. Samson, the Philistines upon you."

The lone man trudged on among his enemies, stumbled a little as feet used only to the hollowness of the ox path felt for the next flat step. He felt the eyes of thousands upon him.

"There must be thousands here," he mumbled to the boy.

"I just heard somebody say three thousand on the roof

alone," the boy said proudly. "Everybody's here. But down here these are just the common people; the lords and princes and their ladies are up on the roof."

"Will you be taking me right up on the roof?" Samson asked anxiously.

"Oh, no—not right away. First you've got to entertain the people down here. You first play your harp for them, then later you're to go up on the roof and sing your song to Delilah."

"Where are you taking me now?"

"To the two great pillars that the whole temple rests on. They want you right there in the center, because you've got to be the center of things. They want you to stand between the pillars, because the crowds are so big they're going to have the people file by you—they can't hold them all in the temple."

"All right, take me there," Samson said listlessly, but he stumbled on the top step in his eagerness.

The boy led the way through the crowded temple. "Here they are," the boy said at last. "Here are the pillars. If you're tired, you can lean against one of them, Samson."

Clumsily blind, Samson stumbled forward, started to fall toward the pillar, blindly grabbed it with both hands, wrapped his arms around it to hold himself up. The crowd laughed. Samson scrambled erect, pulled himself up, but as he did so his hands slid along the pillar, felt a joint between two enormous cylinders of stone; his nails scratched down into another groove between two stones. Now he straightened himself. "Amazing," he said breathlessly. "Am I right? Are these pillars made up of big cut cylinders of stone like that all the way up?"

"Yes, all the way up," the boy said proudly. He gazed up and counted half aloud. "Oh, there must be fifteen-eighteen of them all the way to the roof to hold up the roof and the roof garden."

Samson reached out and up as if curious. "Hey, is that the other pillar? Are they that close together? And just the two of them here in the middle holding everything up? Amazing, amazing! I suppose the architect is up there too with the lords and Delilah. He must be quite a man. Maybe I'll get to meet him." He chattered to the boy, briefly felt of the other pillar, slid his hand up and down, then immediately let his hand fall. "I hope there's room between them for me," he chatted busily. "All this crowd, and me not being able to see them—that way I wouldn't be underfoot."

"Oh, sure," the boy said proudly, "just room enough. And that's exactly where they want you—between the pillars, and the people will come marching by." He took hold of Samson's arm and guided him, really backed him between the pillars. "You'll try to play well, won't you, Samson?" he pleaded anxiously. "Otherwise they'll just take it out on me."

"I practiced hard, didn't I?" Samson said. "Of course, I'm not much of a player. But don't worry, I won't let you down. Not you."

"Start playing then," the boy said urgently. "Here comes a company of soldiers with a captain—I suppose to clear a path for the people to walk by you."

Between the enormous pillars, Samson took up the little

harp, held it before his sightless face, then at his first touch broke two of the strings.

"Oh, Samson," the boy said, dismayed. "Are you nervous? Look what you did!"

There came the harsh authoritative voice of the captain. The detachment of soldiers snapped to a halt. "What's wrong here?" the captain asked the boy. "Why isn't he playing?"

"Oh, sir, he accidentally snapped two of the strings. . . . But I can go and get more."

"Run then," the captain said. "Make it fast. The orders are changed. The overlords and princes can't wait to have him sing to Delilah. They want to have some fun with him first. After that he can entertain the peasants down here the rest of the day for all they care."

The boy raced away. Samson tried to follow the sound of his feet in the little island of military quiet around him, but beyond were the shrieks and drunken laughter and the babel of voices. Then the captain called the boy back. "Bring the harp here," he shouted. "I'll find out if they up there want him to play on three strings until you get back. Now hurry."

Samson heard the boy scrape to a halt, set the little harp against one of the pillars, and turn and dash away again. The captain was instructing one of his soldiers to inform someone on the roof that there would be a delay, unless the lords and ladies wanted Samson to play for them on three strings. Now the captain talked to Samson. "Play," he ordered.

"Play? What with?" Samson said insolently.

"Is that a way to talk to the captain?" a soldier said. "Pick up your harp."

"Maybe you should help him find it," the captain said meaningfully.

Samson heard the slight, stealthy footfall behind him. Then a savage shove sent him sprawling, a booted foot kicked him down as he stumbled forward. Samson fell headlong. The crowd roared. Samson lay helplessly on the floor, feeling for the little harp. But when his groping fingers touched it, someone kicked it from under his hand. The crowd screamed with laughter. Now someone kicked the harp back. It struck Samson in one of his eyeless sockets. The blood spurted. Samson tried to push himself up, but set his hand on the harp, rammed his hand through the remaining strings.

"Waitress," the captain shouted. "A waitress here. A drink here. It looks like the hulk is really hurt."

Samson managed to get to his knees, waited in his kneeling position, sightless, bleeding face lifted to the crowd. He heard a small tinkle of glass. Now a waitress stooped over him. "Oh, Samson." She thrust a cold, wet towel against his sightless eye socket. "Oh, what they are doing to you," she whispered. She crouched down over him as if to hide him from the crowd. "I was a little child in Gaza the night you lifted the iron gates of the town right off their hinges, and carried them up on a mountain. There the gate was the next morning, balanced on the peak of a mountain. Oh, and after that I dreamed of you. I was supposed to be very scared of you, but I always wanted to see you. I didn't think that someday I'd find you like this, and be serving you a drink."

"No drink," Samson muttered. "A little water. Only a

little water, but no drink, for I am a Nazarite to the Lord God of Israel."

"Again," he said within himself. "Please, God, let me be a Nazarite again. Just for this moment. Great God of Israel—just for this moment be my God."

"I have no water on my tray," the waitress patiently repeated.

"Is the boy keeper gone?" Samson asked. "Do you know?"

"Yes, I saw him running down the temple steps."

"He might be getting back, now that there's been this delay," Samson said anxiously. "Will you run out and try to meet him and tell him that I need three more strings—I broke them all. . . . May you go outside the temple?"

"Oh, yes."

"Then please go. Please hurry. And go way down the street. You two. You two who showed me kindness."

He heard the waitress put her tray down beside the pillar, he heard her quick feet going away. He waited a little while—now she, too, must be outside the temple. He dropped the towel she had given him. He placed his arms around the two pillars as if to help him painfully drag himself up on his feet. His hands slid midway between two of the mortared grooves, so that his arms would be around the middle of two of the cylinders of stone. Then he arose.

Now Samson hunched himself, bowed himself. He shook his head and tossed his mane of hair, and then his defiant words roared out of him in such a mighty roar, his voice stilled the temple. "I will shake myself," Samson roared out at the crowd. "And yet again I will shake myself." He tossed his head until his grimy long locks flew from pillar to pillar and swished against the rough stone.

He set his feet against the bases of the pillars, and his great arms cramped around the two cylinders of stone, and now he roared the street call, the song of Delilah, back at the Philistines. "Samson, the Philistines upon you. So let it be. So let it be. The Philistines be upon me!" As he roared out his defiance he brought the two cylinders of the pillars toward him in a great hunching straining of all his strength.

For a moment, for the gasp of a beginning moment, there hung the pillars, a gap in them, as Samson ripped the two huge cylinders of stone out of them and hugged them against his great chest. In open-mouthed awe and unbelief the soldiers, the people, stared at the gap in the pillars that brief gasp of a moment. The gasp was over as it began. Above and around was another roar and a grinding and tearing as the whole temple of Dagon collapsed. The roar of crumbling stone almost drowned the screaming of the hurtling bodies, and the roar of stone was in Samson's ears as the roof and the walls and bodies of the thousands brought down by Samson came down upon Samson. The roar was in his ears as he went down with them—his God had heard his prayer.

THE GIANT

Now the Philistines gathered together their armies to battle. And Saul and the men of Israel were gathered together, and pitched by the valley of Elah, and set the battle in array against the Philistines. And the Philistines stood on a mountain on the one side, and Israel stood on a mountain on the other side: and there was a valley between them.

And there went out a champion out of the camp of the Philistines named Goliath, of Gath, whose height was six cubits and a span. And the staff of his spear was like a weaver's beam; and one bearing a shield went before him. And he stood and cried unto the armies of Israel, and said unto them, "I defy the armies of Israel this day; give me a man, that we may fight together."

When Saul and all Israel heard those words of the Philistine, they were dismayed and greatly afraid.

Now David was the son of that Ephratite of Bethlehem-judah, whose name was Jesse: and he had eight sons. And the three eldest went and followed Saul to the battle. And David was the youngest.

(And the Philistine drew near morning and evening, and presented himself forty days.)

And Jesse said unto David his son, "Take now these ten loaves, and run to the camp to thy brethren, and look how thy brethren fare."

And David rose up early in the morning, and went, as Jesse had commanded him. And David left his carriage in the hand of the keeper of the carriage, and ran into the army, and came and saluted his brethren. And as he talked with them, behold, there came up the champion, the Philistine of Gath, Goliath by name.

From I Samuel 17

THE centuries had rolled on, the years, and the ages, and all the generations of man, since that time at the dawn of creation when Adam and Eve, two shamed, naked-feeling people, had rushed in their new clothes of animal hides from the perfect Garden of Eden. Then the struggle and strife had begun—struggle and strife—the whole lot of man.

The centuries rolled on—century upon century—when again Noah and his family, eight people, had stood in a forlorn little group, looking hopefully up at a rainbow in the sky. Just eight—the world's only people.

The years had rolled on again, and the generations of man, when Abraham and Sarah, an old man and an old woman, both in their nineties, had been promised a son. And in that son, Isaac, was to be the beginning of a nation—a special nation which was to inherit a special land—the land of Canaan. But, instead of inheriting the promised land immediately, the centuries rolled on into four hundred years of slavery in Egypt. The twelve sons of Jacob and their generations and tribes became slaves. And the special nation which had been promised a special land instead became a slave nation in Egypt.

But then after four hundred years came deliverance from slavery and bondage, the slave nation became a free nation, marched out of Egypt, and began the conquest of Canaan, the promised land.

The centuries rolled on, the years, and the generations, and still, after the conquest of Canaan, Israel did not possess all of the promised land. It had to share Canaan with the heathen. And the heathen nations of Canaan which Israel could never quite conquer rose up in their turn and conquered Israel again and again. Conquered, enslaved, and oppressed Israel. Then in Israel judges would rise up—mighty men, mighty to deliver—and under the judges Israel beat back the oppressing heathen nations. But the judges died and passed on, and always some other heathen Canaanite nation would come up to conquer and enslave Israel again.

Now it was the turn of the Philistines, the cruel Philistines against whom mighty Samson had warred singlehanded and alone. But Samson had gone down with the Philistines in the fall of the great temple of Dagon, and now it was the time of the last judge in Israel—Samuel. The last judge was no warrior, Samuel was a tired old man. And under Samuel the people of Israel demanded a king—a young, strong man to lead them in battle. At the behest of the people and at the command of God, Samuel had anointed Saul as the first king over Israel. Samuel was judge, Saul was king.

The Israelites were elated—for the first time in their long history Israel had a king, just like all the other nations of Canaan. Now at last they felt themselves to be a real nation with a government and a king—a continuing government that wouldn't be dependent on judges that might or might not rise up. Kings succeeded kings, the sons succeeded the royal fathers. And now Israel had its first king.

But Israel's elation was sobered, for, although they now were a nation with a king, they were not a free nation. The Philistines possessed most of Israel. Not only had the Philistines overrun Israel, the Philistines had possession of the sacred ark of the covenant. The ark of God which had brought down the walls of Jericho was in a heathen land, in a heathen temple. Dagon, the fish god of the Philistines, had seemingly triumphed over the ark of the covenant of the God of Israel. The Philistines were in Israel, the ark was in the land of the Philistines.

It was a queer mixed-up time. The times were out of joint. Israel was for the first time in its history a nation with a king, yet as a nation—if it were a nation, and not just a colony of the Philistines—Israel was at its lowest ebb. Instead of conquering all of Canaan, the Israelites were being conquered tribe by tribe by the Philistines, and now the Philistines had come up against the tribe of Judah. After all the ages and the centuries, the possession of the promised land of Canaan seemed farther out of Israel's reach than ever before.

In this strange time of the last judge and the first king, a strange battle was going on, and, although led by Saul, the first King of Israel, it wasn't really a battle at all. It was a stalemate. No swords clashed, no shields clanged, and no spears or arrows flew. For forty days the army of Israel and the army of the Philistines had stood in battle array, each on a hill with a valley between them, a valley through which flowed a little brook. But it was such a strange, quiet, immobilized battle that for forty days both armies could hear the rushing of the little brook in the valley between the camps of the two armies.

All because of one man! There still were giants in the land of Canaan in these days. And the fear of giants, which had once under Moses turned the people of Israel away from Canaan and back into the wilderness for forty years, once again paralyzed an army of Israel and its king into doing nothing for forty days. At the scene of battle, there was no sound of battle—just the sound of a rushing brook.

And there he came—the giant. Goliath of Gath, the Philistine. Again this day he came striding down the hill from the camp of the Philistines, as he had done now for thirty-nine days. A true giant, Goliath came striding and took such steps that his shield-bearer—a full-grown man—had to run along beside him like a little child. The man staggered under the weight of Goliath's great shield, but still he had to keep up with the giant. Goliath took a single step over the little brook, and let his shield-bearer struggle through the brook the best he could. The giant strode a few paces up the hill of the Israelites, then he stopped and in a great hoarse roar of a voice he began cursing the army of Israel, and Israel's God, until he ran out of words.

It was a daily performance. It had gone on so long—twice a day for thirty-nine days—the soldiers in the Israelite camp had almost grown used to it. At first they had fled, but now after all the days only a few little groups of soldiers came to the edge of the camp to look down at the giant. Behind the little groups, the daily business of camp life went on as usual.

Below the hill the giant fell silent; he'd run out of rantings and cursings. He looked helplessly down at his shield-bearer as if asking for more words to shout up the hill.

The giant looked almost indignantly back up at the little

groups on the top of the hill standing idly watching him—what was the use of challenging them once again to hand-to-hand combat? Not a single man in the camp had dared to take a step down the hill in thirty-nine days, they weren't likely to do so today. They didn't answer him, they didn't even move, nothing stirred. Goliath stood looking around.

Now toward the camp of the Israelites came a boy on a wagon drawn by an old mule. Goliath idly watched him. Now the mule reached the trench the Israelites had dug around their camp at the top of the hill. Just to amuse himself the giant let out a great raw roar. The mule staggered up, almost plunged in the ditch, but the startled boy in the bucking wagon didn't look at the mule; the boy sat turned in the seat, staring in open-mouthed awe at the roaring giant below the hill.

The giant laughed. "Who are you?" he roared out at the boy.

"I am David, son of Jesse, the Bethlehemite," the boy obediently answered back, voice shrill with awe. "I just came to camp to bring my three brothers some loaves of bread."

A man rushed down the hill, jumped the ditch, and grabbed the mule, said quick things to David. Now the boy scrambled down from the wagon, jumped the ditch, and ran up the hill to the first little group at the edge of the camp. The man—as red-headed as the boy—it must be one of his brothers—led the mule and the wagon away.

On top of the hill in the safety of the group of idle soldiers, the awed boy turned again to look down at the giant. The giant glared up at him. "But who is that?" the boy asked loudly.

In the quiet valley the giant heard every word. "That is Goliath of Gath," the group told the red-headed boy. "For forty days now he's been doing that. Twice a day, morning and evening, he comes out to curse us and our God, and to challenge somebody—anybody—to come out to do battle with him."

"Look at that spear," the boy said unbelievingly. "Why, it's as thick as an ox yoke! How big is he anyway?"

"Whyn't you run down and measure him?" some joker told him.

But the boy, David, didn't seem to hear, couldn't take his eyes off the giant. "Why, he must be at least nine feet tall. What a terrible man! But look at that spear! How many has he killed these forty days with that spear?"

"Not a man," they told him.

"Not a single man?"

"No, for the simple, good reason that not a man in this army has been foolish enough to get within reach of that spear."

"And he comes out twice a day challenging you, and cursing our God and our army and our king? And nobody does anything?"

"No. Why? What would you want to do? Do you want to go down there?"

"Yes," David said.

"Hey, Goliath—Goliath," a soldier yelled out. "Here's a boy wants to do battle with you."

"All of him, all of the boy?" Goliath roared back.

A crowd gathered on top of the hill. Goliath stood looking up, silent and amused. He said something to his shield-bearer, and the man laughed. But now, on top of the hill, David's soldier brothers joined the crowd. One of them, almost old enough to be David's father, elbowed his way through the crowd, and grabbed David by the shoulder. "Look, you little fool," he said, angry and loud. "Can't you see you're making a fool of yourself? You fight Goliath? You've run your little errand. Now get your wagon and get back to tending your bunch of sheep in Bethlehem."

But the soldier crowd would have none of it; they wouldn't let David go—they were having fun, this was a break in the monotony of forty days. "If the shepherd boy wants to fight Goliath, let's take him to Saul. The king should be pleased—a challenger at last. He isn't quite as big as Goliath—about up to his knees, would you say?—well, it's the best we've got. On to Saul with him."

Eliab, the older brother, fumed and raged, but the soldiers took over, shoved him aside, led David to Saul.

King Saul was either desperate, or he fell in with the tomfoolery of the soldier crowd that brought David before him. It was at least a change to hear his demoralized soldiers joking about Goliath instead of running and crawling out of sight when the giant roared in the valley.

The towering Saul could hardly keep from smiling as he looked down on the earnest, determined, red-headed boy. "You want to fight Goliath all by yourself?"

"I once fought a lion all by myself," David said eagerly. "I grabbed the lion by the beard . . ."

He couldn't finish because of the laughter. "You'll have to jump mighty high to grab Goliath by the beard. . . . Bring him a ladder!"

David turned to the man. "No, I won't need a ladder. I'll bring his beard down to me."

Saul looked at David. "Well, at least you've courage—that's something new." He turned to his men. "All right then, you heroes, bring the armor out of my tent, and put it on him. . . . Maybe if Goliath sees a mere boy in armor come out to him, Goliath might go into such a rage it might give him a stroke."

They actually brought out Saul's huge armor; they hung it over David's slight shoulders. Everybody laughed, only David's three brothers looked on red-faced and silent and shamed. In the armor David tried to take a step. "It's too heavy," he muttered. "I can't move in this."

"How heavy was that lion?" somebody called out.

David was almost in tears. "Let me go as I am, sir," he begged Saul. "I'm not used to armor and heavy weapons."

Saul shook his head. "I don't know," he began doubtfully.

But Goliath down in the valley decided it for them. "Well, is that boy coming, or isn't he?" he yelled up into the camp. "It's hot down in this valley, and I'm broiling inside of this armor—it feels like a furnace. And after forty days of this

I'll even fight a boy. I'm sick of it—I seem to be the only one in the Philistine army that has to work. Every day and twice a day I march down this miserable hill—and march up again. The rest of our army doesn't even bother to put on armor—they know none of you cowards dare fight me anyway. So bring on the boy—it would be a change. I'm sick of shouting words they put into my mouth, I wouldn't mind a little action. I'm a simple man—I understand action. Bring on the boy."

To Goliath's unbelieving surprise a whole crowd of soldiers came moving toward the edge of the camp at the top of the hill. And ahead of them they pushed the red-headed boy. But all the boy had was his shepherd's staff, and all he wore was his simple shepherd's smock that hardly came down to his knees. The crowd stopped on top of the hill, the boy came on alone.

Goliath shoved his heavy, hot helmet back from his forehead, gazed up in astounded unbelief. "What is this—some silly trick?" he roared up at the Israelites.

He turned to his shield-bearer. "Come on," he said impatiently. "I can't fight a boy with a stick." He stepped over the brook.

"There must be more to it than this," the shield-bearer called out after Goliath. "It's some kind of a trick." He scrambled through the brook after Goliath.

The puzzled, indignant giant strode away, the shield-bearer hustled to catch up with him, but across the brook they both turned at the same time in their puzzlement and stood watching the red-headed boy.

Behind them David had run down to the brook. Now he waded bare-legged, and stooped and searched for little stones. Oh, he must have a sling like all shepherds had—just a shepherd boy with a staff and a sling gathering some nice, smooth stones to use to guide his sheep when he got back to them. Goliath turned to stride up the hill, but suddenly it enraged him—that boy coolly choosing stones from the bottom of the brook—acting as if he, the most fearsome man in all Canaan, was about as fearsome as a sick ox.

"I'll scare the hide off him," he muttered to the shield-bearer. But even Goliath's mutter was a near roar, and in the brook David straightened up and looked at him.

The enraged giant whirled, took three awful strides toward the boy in the brook. David splashed toward the far bank, grabbed his shepherd's staff up out of the grass, as if to fend off the giant with it. It was the insult supreme.

Goliath stopped in his tracks. "What am I then? A dog, that you come after me with a stick?" The giant hefted his spear, raised his enormous spear as if to transfix David with it.

But instead of dissolving in fear and awe as the giant had expected, David dropped his staff, turned and came rushing back through the brook toward Goliath. "Hah, big giant, you have to come at me with a spear and a man to hold a shield in front of you, but I'm right now coming at you with a sling and stone, and I'm coming at you in the name of the Lord of hosts and the God of the armies of Israel."

The giant took one big infuriated step, David hurriedly dropped a stone in his shepherd's sling, came clambering up

out of the brook, came running at the giant, his sling swinging. He swung the sling back and forth, getting the feel and the heft of it for the aim. The giant stood open-mouthed, dumbfounded at the foolish courage of the boy. The shield-bearer stopped beside him. The boy swung the sling. The little stone crashed against Goliath's forehead, imbedded itself in the giant's forehead. Goliath dazedly pawed at his bruised forehead, brushed the little stone away, but as he did so he crashed forward, fell as a tree falls. The horrified shield-bearer fled up the hill, let the stunned, helpless giant lay.

The giant came out of his daze, stirred, groaned, rolled a little—his great hands dug into the grass and sand. He tried to raise himself, but a great weight seemed to be on his back. A roaring was in his ears, and a slight scraping sound was among the roaring. He tried to puzzle it out, but dazed and broken he could not puzzle out what the sound was, what the slight scraping, what the weight. And he never did puzzle it out that the weight on his back was David, and that the scraping sound was the sound of his own sword being dragged out of the giant scabbard by David. The giant felt only the searing of the cold edge of steel on his neck that immediately became a hot, roaring pain. Then the giant knew no more—forevermore.

The Philistines on the one hill, the Israelites on the other, saw the stunning development—the giant gone down, the giant gone headless. A shout roared up from the camp of Israel. The Israelites poured down the hill, they swept by the fallen giant and the red-headed boy, swept up the hill of the Philistines.

The Philistine army had completely depended on their giant, Goliath. Now in the unforeseen turn of events they stood as if paralyzed—unready, unprepared, demoralized. They fled. They fled and the army of Israel pursued. The Israelites drove them out of the land, drove them back into Philistia, drove them as far as Gath, the town of Goliath.

Only David stayed behind with the body of Goliath. He had no arms with which to fight, except for the sword and the spear of Goliath, but they were too heavy.

At last the victorious army of Israel returned to the site of the camp on the hill to collect the spear and the sword and the armor of Goliath, and Goliath's head—and David.

In triumph the red-headed boy in his simple shepherd's tunic rode next to King Saul as the victorious army marched through the towns and the cities of Israel. At the gate of every town the women and girls swept out to meet the army with Saul and David riding at its head, and to stare in awe at the gruesome, leering head of Goliath speared on the point of David's shepherd's staff. The women swept out of the towns and through the gates to meet their men in victory. They came dancing with timbrels and tabrets, they came singing. The women came with a victory song they had made in praise of their men, and of their heroes. And this is the song that the women sang:

Saul has slain his thousands
But David his ten thousands.

And all through the town, and in every town, the proud women ran along beside the line of march shaking their tabrets and shrilling their song. And, though the women did not know, their song was more than a song, for it was a prophecy. For here riding through their towns, riding beside King Saul, came more than a red-headed shepherd boy who had slain Goliath. Here came the conqueror. Here came a boy who in the years still to come was to accomplish what had not been accomplished even by the great Joshua—the conquest of all Canaan. Here came the boy who after all the roll of the centuries was to fulfill the promise of God made to Abraham, and give Israel its promised land of Canaan as a whole land—and as their land.

After the centuries, under this boy as their future king, Israel was at last to have rest from its enemies, and an end to struggle and strife. Israel was at last to inherit peace, every man under his vine and under his fig tree in a quiet land of peace. And here riding with Saul at the head of the army came the boy who was to bring it about. And the army marched and the women sang as if they knew that now at last truly a giant was in the land—David, the king and the conqueror.

DeJong, Meindert, 1910–
The mighty ones; great men and women of early Bible days. Pictures by Harvey Schmidt. New York, Harper [1959]

278 p. illus. 25 cm.

1. Bible. O. T.—History of Biblical events—Fiction. I. Title.

PZ3.D3666Mi 221.95 59–5314 ‡

Library of Congress